Glimpses of the Association Between Fairy Tales and Homoeopathy

by

Dr Farokh J Master

Editor:

Dr Geeta Rani Arora

Homeopathic Essence

GLIMPSES OF THE ASSOCIATION BETWEEN FAIRY TALES AND HOMOEOPATHY

First Edition: 2013
1st Impression: 2013

Published by Kuldeep Jain for

Homeopathic Essence
An Imprint of
B. JAIN PUBLISHERS (P) LTD.
1921/10, Chuna Mandi, Paharganj, New Delhi–110 055 (INDIA)
Tel.: +91-11-4567 1000; Fax: +91-11-4567 1010
Email: info@bjain.com; Website: www.bjain.com

ISBN: 978-81-319-1174-7

Foreword

A very interesting work by Farokh Master on our age old favourite fairy tales. The famous Mumbai homoeopath explores our human soul and its very inner essence to simplify the understanding of Homoeopathic remedies through these simple tales. It helps us understand the minds of our patients through these characters. An enjoyable read!!

Dr Didier Grandgeorge

Preface

The last decade has seen an amazing transformation and broadening in the ways fairy tales are interpreted and understood. This book brings together the most recent developments in the archetypal patterns in fairy tales, while taking into account the complexity of the emerging field. I hope it will prove to be accessible at all levels.

This book is the fruit of my long journey of thirty years studying analytical psychology. I, as a homoeopath took this study to help my patients grow regarding their's and society's psychological realities, find healing and meaning in their lives, greater depth in their relationships and to live in response to their newly discovered sense of purpose.

The book is a collection of fairy tale interpretations keeping homoeopathic philosophy, materia medica and repertory as it's base. I chose only a few fairy tales that challenged as they were unusual. I wanted to show how Jung's method of interpreting archetypal fantasy material could be applied to these diverse tales.

The book is written equally for homoeopaths involved with Jungian analytical methods as well as for homoeopaths who know nothing regarding psychotherapy and psychology.

I have equally used works of Bruno Bettelheim, Carl Jung and Marie Louise von Franz while explaining the motif's in fairy tales. I have tried my best to offer insights into the psychology of all the characters, especially the central characters like the prince, princess, king, step-mother. While others reflect the problems and characteristics of the anima, the inner femininity of man.

I have drawn images of homoeopathic drug pictures at every stage while describing archetypes and symbolic themes that appear in fairy tales.

Synthesis repertory, edited by Dr Frederick Schroyens has been the prime source from which a lot of information regarding individual drugs has been extracted.

I am grateful to the Grimm brothers and Hans Christian Andersen for making the world richer by writing such stories for generations to come.

I have gained this insight through my life's experiences and analysis, through working with my patients, and through my studies.

I would like to thank Dr Ameet Panchal, my student and now my colleague for stimulating me to study psychology. He came to my clinic to study homoeopathy but instead taught me and stimulated me to study this fascinating science of analytical psychology.

I also learnt a lot from another good soul – Dr Farokh Buchia. He always encouraged me to understand a close link between homoeopathy and psychology.

Dr Farhad Adajania has always helped me with his sincere suggestions and healthy comments.

I am also grateful to my darling daughter, Dr Rukshin Master for going through the manuscript and making the necessary corrections.

Mr Rene Otter, Dr Frederick Schroyens, Dr Dider Grandgeorge, Dr Edouard Broussalian gave me a wonderful atmosphere in Holland, France and Switzerland to write this book.

My clinic staff needs a special thanks, especially Dr Shivin Gupta who kept on helping me whenever I was stuck with Microsoft word, Dr Natasha Fernandes helping me to repertorize the cases, Miss Sunita Shah for all her help in graphics and designing the cover page. Dr Fatema Slatewala who helped me very sincerely to edit the stories from the source books.

Above all, I want to thank my analysand's students, seminar participants for their uncounted contribution in raising questions and challenges, for permitting me to use their material and for offering their feelings, reactions and thoughts in the course of therapy.

Last but not the least I want to thank my wife Dilnavaz and my two queens of heart Rukshin and Mahaziver who dedicated their love so that I can write this book.

Publisher's Note

Dr Farokh Master is one of the living stalwarts of Homoeopathy today. He has written more than 63 books and lectures in most of the countries where homoeopathy exists in the world. We are very proud to be the publishers of his works. This work of Dr Farokh is a masterpiece where he has shared his experience of more than 34 years of practice on use of fairy tales in interpreting the psychology of the person.

The book starts with the factual and historical details about how the famous works on fairy tales came into publishing like the Grimm's Brother & Oscar Wilde. Further it discusses the different aspects of fairy tales and what impact they have on a child psychology. The book discusses how people relate to different characters of fairy tales and how we can use that to understand the psychology of the person and also find the most probable homoeopathy remedy on that basis. The homoeopathic interpretation of various characters of fairy tales has been talked about which is a very interesting read.

We hope this books brings more insights into homoeopathic practice and thus help homoeopaths heal more and more people through this wonderful science.

Kuldeep Jain
CEO, B. Jain Publishers (P) Ltd.

Contents

CHAPTER 1

Introduction To Fairy Tales

As with most children, my journey into the land of fairy tales started at a very tender age. We were four siblings and I was the youngest, born after a long gap of nine years. I was overly protected by my mother, and so, as a child I was very sensitive, fearful and delicate. Also, as a child I was very curious about things. Hence, I would ask many questions and at the end of the day my mother would run out of answers. Then to keep my active mind occupied she started telling me stories — stories of kings and queens, gnomes and elves, giants and witches, princes and princesses, nymphs and demons, fairies and godmothers, the list was endless. I would hear them with rapt attention, and would picture them all in my imaginative mind. The other two people instrumental in feeding my imagination were Mrs Rita Modi, my Montessori teacher, and Naval uncle who was a lonely old bachelor and loved me like his own son. They too had lots of stories to tell and sometimes they would animate the characters and bring them to life for that short while. Thus, an insatiable interest in stories was developed in me in my formative years. Later this passion grew and was responsible for my avid interest in reading anything from comics to stories with suspense, drama or crime.

Then, there came a period when I had to give up my passion for story reading, as academic responsibilities used to take up most of my time. As fate would have it, after completing my Intermediate, I took up homoeopathy. While studying the homoeopathic materia medica, I had to again go through the fairy tales, but this time with a much deeper understanding of the symbolic meaning behind them. Precisely at that time, I had decided that I would one day pen these thoughts into words and bring out a book on these symbolic meanings behind the fairy tales.

Moreover, after the birth of my two daughters — Rukshin and Mahaziver, I could revisit all those stories I had put away. I could now enjoy imparting my delight in fairy tales to my children. Telling stories to my daughters was quite fascinating for me as well as for them.

For hundreds of years, fairy tales have been read by children and adults alike, instructing, fascinating and horrifying us by turns. As both readers and writers, we return to their themes again and again, gleaning new meaning from each narration. There are many excellent resources, both online and in print, which can assist the recreational reader, the parent, the teacher, or the student of fairy tales. This pathfinder endeavours to describe and categorize these resources, in order to facilitate both the study and the enjoyment of these remarkable stories.

Fairy tales have been with us for a very long time, and undoubtedly will remain with us for years to come. Even today, as many of these resources show, more stories of this kind are being written every year, some based on legendary tales, others completely new. They are enjoyable to read, frequently educational, and can be fascinating to research.

The key moment in a familiar fairy tale carries many insights. It is, at once, a commentary on social values, a vivid example of family tragedy and a bit of personal psychology.

Folklore is compacted wisdom, literature that yields more information with each reading. There is much we can learn by reflecting on the stories heard in childhood. Magical characters such as the Pied Piper, the Talking Frog and the Fairy Godmother are likely to remain in our imagination for a lifetime. The adventures these stories describe often reflect challenges we face in our journeys today. The tales hide a wealth of insights just below the surface. They are clearly more than mere entertainment for children.

The storytellers intentionally loaded the adventures with heavy symbolism to reveal more meanings as we develop a deeper awareness of ourselves. Bedtime stories have an enormous influence over our identities, as we identify with certain characters in the stories which we heard in our childhood. To some degree, many live out these stories, largely unaware of how much the old tales may be shaping their lives. It is a great treasure to know and reveal which tales from our childhood have a hold on us. Mythical stories make up a kind of collective dream that we all have together. If we want to understand our dreams, in many respects, we can look at these stories and study them. If we want to understand the stories better, we can study our dreams. There is a great inter-relationship between these two forms of our imagination.

A talking animal in a story is often the voice of nature. Among other messages, we are being reminded that we are also animals. We are walking around in animal flesh. We sometimes forget this in our excessively mental, all too industrial culture. We are, first of all, animal creatures. We are not just visitors of nature, or merely caretakers of nature. We are nature. Guiding animals are crucial in mythical stories. Psychologically, this might well represent the wisdom of the body. Sinister or wicked characters may represent aspects of us that have been neglected or rejected.

Carl Jung noted that the shadow energies, those energies that people are completely unaware of, in dreams and stories, often appear as threatening witches or wolves. Jung insisted that something good can come from this darkness. Something valuable waits for us in the shadow. We are not to exclude that from how we define ourselves. Ultimately, inclusion is the goal. The challenge is to integrate these elements into our identity in a constructive manner. The darker elements in some tales often reveal shadow energies in an action, an image, or even a setting. For example, the deep, dark forest is a common representation of the feared elements within. The forest can reflect parts of us that are never entirely tamed and are always somewhat dangerous and chaotic. These elements sometimes come up in our nightmares. They are important parts of us and in some ways they are the most creative aspects of our inner world. We need to let ourselves go into this dark forest. It is difficult and mysterious, but still, fresh energies and new ideas come from that place. Often we need the experiences in life that seem like setbacks and shadows. These can be difficult times and as our first reaction we wish we could avoid those circumstances but ultimately, on retrospection we realize that those were enormously valuable moments. Such experiences force us to claim aspects of ourselves that we have neglected to develop. We grow to be more than we thought was possible.

There is a tale about a farmer who was ploughing his field. Suddenly, he finds that his plough strikes something. The farmer digs below to see what the plough has snagged on and he finds it has hooked a large ring. He digs further, to free the plough, but sees that the ring is attached to a large flat stone. After digging more, the farmer lifts the stone with the help of the ring. As the stone rises, it reveals an entrance to a deep underground cave filled with treasures. The parable suggests that when something interrupts what we are trying to do, we should not be too sure that this is a negative event. If we look into the impediment to our progress, we may open or find hidden places in our souls and reveal secret riches. After discovering the buried treasure, we have the task of integrating these deep realms of beauty into our daily lives. Learning to interpret stories of adventure is not difficult if one understands symbolism and learns to understand the meaning of each image in the story.

The farmer getting stuck shows how trouble can interrupt our journeys for good reasons that we may not immediately grasp. The tale is a visual experience. Any one of the symbols in a classic story is worthy of a close look. If we meditate on the flow of images, and reflect on the meanings it presents to us, the rewards can be great. Ancient tales have their own lives, each with unique, eccentric qualities. Part of the richness is that the same story will have different lessons for every person who listens.

Fairy tales exercise a draw, a drag, a gravitational pull upon the minds of children and adults alike. Like old alchemical treatises, they seem to offer a way to turn lead into gold, to make one's own life as magical as that, to be found between the lines of their favourite tales.

However, much like those old alchemical treatises, these require translation. Fairy tales and folklore, legends and myths, tales of wonder of every sort and type, are written not only in the mundane languages of the world like French, German, Italian, Spanish and English but also in the language of symbols.

It is said that 'a rose by any other name should be as sweet' in a number of stories. Such roses symbolize innocence (that is, the roses that wreath Sleeping Beauty's kingdom, the rose brought for Beauty by her father from the castle of the Beast).

The themes of these stories frequently demonstrate the values of the culture from where the tales originate. They are mirrors helping to emphasize the true ideals of their societies. For example, a society that emphasizes the worth of virginity produces tales with a preponderance of such symbols of chastity, not only roses, but also blood red cloaks and fragile, transparent, membranous slippers.

Some symbols, however, seem to cross the cultural divide, appearing and reappearing in folk stories across the globe, as the issues which they represent are more or less of universal relevance. Journeys across water and through the woods, transitions and examinations of the unknown, can be found in the folk stories of various Native American tribes, in European fairy tales, in Greek mythologies and in Chinese legends. The details may change. The gender of the travelling protagonist, the terrain that they journey through, the perils which stray their steps and their reasons for doing it all (riches, familial loyalty, true love) are subject to change, but the acknowledgment that change itself is inevitable, are the recurring symbols of their journey.

The stories and tales we loved as children often contain clues about the needs we had at that time. We might not have been in touch with our needs on a conscious level, but they were there none the less. Immersing ourselves in particular realms of story and fantasy met some of these needs. In fact, you can look at the stories you loved as a child to see what those needs might have been. The adventures these stories describe often reflect challenges we face in our journeys. The tales hide a wealth of insights just below their surface. They are clearly more than mere entertainment for children.

All my life I have travelled abroad extensively, primarily to give seminars on homoeopathy but, side by side, I also studied the local folk tales of countries I visited. When I was in Denmark, I visited Hans Christian Andersen's house and learned more of his stories, such as *The Little Mermaid*. In Germany, I went to the village of Hamelin, where the tale of the *Pied Piper of Hamlin* takes place. In each location, I would thoroughly examine a story and the sites associated with it. In Baghdad, it was the *Arabian Nights*. While visiting Greece and Egypt, I would study mythology. In the temples of India and Japan, the tales of Asia came to life. Seeing how the adventures reflected their settings and how the stories are still alive in these places was a powerful experience. It shaped my sense of the world. Different people imagine the tales differently. I had heard the stories before, and had pictures in my mind about what those places would look like but when I saw, for example, the spot in Germany where the Pied Piper supposedly led the children away, it didn't look exactly the same as I had imagined. In a way, noticing

that difference made me aware of how our creativity works. It was a glimpse of the power of imagination. I later learned how these stories portray life issues in miniature. The story of the Pied Piper reminds us that every parent has to deal with letting go of their children at some stage of life, and every former child has to cope with feelings about how it is to leave home. If we take the tale as a reflection of the inner landscape, we see that all the characters can represent aspects of our own personalities. The village leaders may symbolize a practical, thrifty side that does not sufficiently appreciate our magical qualities or artistic abilities. If we cheat our imagination of appropriate time and resources, things may go badly. Creativity and play engage the child-like energies that can leave us in a state of depression if they depart. These tales are psychological mirrors and we become more complex as we mature. The storytellers intentionally loaded the adventures

with heavy symbolism to reveal more meanings as we develop a deeper awareness of ourselves. Bedtime stories have an enormous influence over our identities. People identify with certain characters in the stories they heard in their childhood. To some degree, many live out these stories, largely unaware of how much the old tales may be shaping our lives. It is a great treasure to know and reveal which tales from our childhood have a hold on us. Once the general pattern or storyline becomes evident, the challenge is to participate in rewriting our own story. We may not be able to create the rivers that carry us along but we can certainly navigate the little boats of our lives.

Stories can be like the Holy Grail, which, when passed from person to person, let them drink what they alone desired. Also, when we come back to the same story after a time, it will tell us new things. Stories can speak to us in several ways at once. The practical aspects of our personalities appreciate the assistance they provide in prudent decision making. Our playful, child-like energies find the stories to be great fun. The quiet, spiritual side is grateful to have some time invested in reflection. Poet William Stafford had a favourite image. He said that the work of creativity is to 'follow the golden thread.' Something catches your attention, a feeling, an image, an idea, or the events of a moment. The challenge is to pay attention to that subtle urge and follow it gently. We must roll out the golden thread with care or it will break. Opening ourselves to greater significance in familiar stories requires a certain tenderness of spirit. The notions will be fragile at first and we must hold them gently for some time until they deliver their message to us. The effects of what we learn might well last for a lifetime.

CHAPTER 2

Fairy Tales And
The Unconscious

The symbolic interpretation of fairy tales as well as their relation to the unconscious has become a challenging field of speculations for a number of Freudian and Jungian analysts for example, Bettelheim, 1976; Dundes, 1989; Kaes et al, 1989; Kast, 1995; La Genardiere, 1996; Von Franz, 1982.

Freud was the first to discover the symbolic nature of fairy tales. Like myths and legends, fairy tales touch the most primitive parts of the psyche. In the *'Interpretation of Dreams,* 1900' Freud turns to fairy tales to advance dream analysis. In the *'Wolf Man'* (1918), he argues that the fairy tale offers the child a way of thinking which corresponds to the representation of himself. The child identifies with the wild animal and that perhaps explains his lack of surprise to the anthropomorphic animals found in many tales.

Roheim (1953), maintains that fairy tales resemble dream experiences. He argues that a large part of mythology is derived from dreams. Thus, fairy tales are probably the outcome of dream experiences spread by the word of mouth. Furthermore, according to Swartz (1956), the fairy tale — like dreams,

a. Deal with opposites or contrasts

b. Are illogical

c. Have manifest and latent meaning

d. Use symbolisms

e. Expound and expand the concept of reality

f. Are a dramatized form of expression,

g. Contain sexual as well as cultural elements

h. Express wishes

i. Have humour, and

j. Employ the mechanism of condensation, substitution, displacement, devaluation and over evaluation.

More recently, Cramer (1991), noted that the defense mechanisms of denial, projection and identification may be encountered in a number of popular fairy tales.

Kaes et al. (1989), suggests that fairy tales are the closest to dreams in terms of it's content, it's processes and it's subjective usage. According to these authors, fairy tales serve three functions: as a link, as a transformation, and as an intermediary. More explicitly, they link primary with secondary processes; they transform unconscious fantasies to structured narrations whereby the form and symbolisms express underlying desires; finally, the tale acts as an intermediary between the body and the social milieu.

Ferenczi, (1913/1919), proposes that fairy tales represent a return to the stage of the omnipotence of the self. 'In fairy tales, the fantasies of omnipotence continue to reign... (page 65). While in reality we feel weak, fairy tale heroes are strong and invincible; while our actions and thoughts are limited by time and space, in the fairy tale world we live eternally, we can be at a million places at the same time, we can foresee the future and we have the knowledge of our past. Bettelheim's book 'The Uses of Enchantment, 1976' has become a landmark in the psychoanalytic theory of fairy tales. The book offers an elaborate account of the relation between children and fairy tales, placing special emphasis on the therapeutic value of the latter, for the child. Bettelheim produces extensive analyses of popular tales and attempts to demonstrate how each one of these reflects conflicts or anxieties at specific stages of development.

According to Shapiro and Katz (1978), Bettelheim interprets the symbolic meaning of the fairy tale on three levels. First, a character is discussed as representing crucial others in the child's life; second, as representing an experienced part of the personality (good or bad self) and finally, as representing internal processes (id, ego and superego).

Jung attributed special importance to fairy tales when he claimed that in these stories one could best study the comparative anatomy of the psyche. In myths and legends one gets all the basic patterns of the psyche through an overlay of cultural material; in fairy tales there is much less specific conscious cultural material.

All fairy tales attempt to describe one psychic reality — the self, while many fairy tales symbolically describe the initial stage in the process of individuation — the achievement of self-realization, by telling of a king who has fallen ill or grown old. The ego is usually represented by the hero and thus considered as the restorer of the healthy personality.

Though nearly all tales circle around the self - symbol, many stories reflect motifs, which remind us of Jungian concepts such as the shadow, the anima, the animus, or the persona. For example, in the story of Rapunzel, the anima is in the hands of an evil creature (the witch) and then the hero and the anima must escape. That means that the hero has to protect his anima from the evil influence of the unconscious.

The Jungian school of fairy tale analysis has been best represented by Max Luthie (1987), and Marie Louise Von Franz (1982). Von Franz (1982), notes that these tales are the simplest and purest expression of collective unconscious processes. The archetypes are the structural components of the collective unconscious and show the way to transformation and development. Archetypes may find expression through dreams, myths and fairy tales. Among the most well known archetypes are Birth and Rebirth, Death, Unity, the Hero, the Child, God, the Wise Old Man or Woman, the Earth Mother, and the Animal.

Analyzing our favourite childhood stories can help us understand what our hopes, dreams and secret needs were, when we were young. Exploring our childhood through these stories is also a safe way to get back in touch with feelings long buried. Since we're exploring beloved stories rather than the abuse itself, the mind will allow important emotions from this time in our lives to arise, perhaps for the first time. For many women, this is an eye-opening exercise; it can be quite a shock to see how your favourite story, long forgotten, fits quite exactly with the circumstances of your childhood now that you remember the abuse.

CHAPTER 3

The Modified Fairy Tale Test (MFTT)

Since the past few years, I have started using toys to interpret the unconscious mind of little kids. Over a period of years I started collecting toys used by child psychologists to interpret children's minds. The toys consist of father, mother, brother, sister, family, grandparents, fairies, fairy tale figures like Cinderella, Red Riding Hood, Robin Hood, Snow White, Sleeping Beauty, etc., different types of wild and domestic animals, witches, demons, ghost, dragons, dwarves, etc.

Some of the interpretations are mentioned below and are derived from children's responses to a projective personality test. The main advantage of projective techniques is that they facilitate the projection of unconscious feelings and attitudes onto the stimulus material.

Mostly these tests are performed on children between 7 and 12 years of age. It's conception rests on the association between fairy tales and unconscious processes (for example – Bettelheim, 1976, Kaes et al., 1989). It's broader purpose is to help the homoeopath assess the child's personality dynamics, offering information not just about isolated personality parameters, but also about their inter-relations.

The test material consists of placing different toys on the table and asking the child to pick his favourite one from the lot and say a few words on what he/she feels about them? Why was that particular toy selected? Are there any good or bad experiences with that toy figure? If an animal figure is selected, then it's nature and their fascination for such a toy is discussed. Finally every child is asked a common question: What does each toy mean? Or what are his/her thought processes related to each toy?

The results bring forth following personality variances, namely:

- Ambivalence
- Different types of motivational aggression
- Fear of aggression
- Anxiety
- Depression
- Self-esteem

Children's responses to questions reflect several latent themes or conflicts for each of the toys.

If a dwarf is selected for example, it may reveal the following:

- Affective needs (the child will take care of them or the dwarfs will take care of the child)
- Fear of possible dangers/insecurities (Snow White may be a thief or the Witch might kill them too)
- Coping with danger (they will kill the Witch, they will find a way of deceiving her or will have the ability to hide)
- Self-image (will doubt their ability to help Snow White, concern about their small stature or their appearance)

If the Witch is selected, the following issues come up for discussion:

- Dominance/ambitions
- Self-image (she is getting old, her magic power is diminishing, nobody loves her, she is ugly)
- Mother - child relationship (motherly image)

- Narcissistic feelings (she wants everyone to admire her)

- Sibling rivalry but (Snow White is the sibling)

- Oedipal feelings (the Witch wants to exterminate Snow White so that she becomes the most beautiful lady in the land)

- Superego (fear of getting punished for her wrongdoings)

- Aggression

If the Giant is selected then issues related to the following topics came up on the surface:

- Aggression

- Dominance

- Oral needs

- Self-image (he is ugly/stupid/big, nobody wants him)

- Father-child relationship (rare)

- Sexual feelings (he wants to find a girlfriend – rare)

If Little Red Riding Hood is selected, the following issues can come up for discussion:

- Mother image

- Severity of superego (she begs mother to forgive her, she wants the story to end because she deserved mother's punishment)

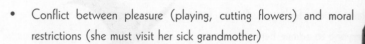

- Conflict between pleasure (playing, cutting flowers) and moral restrictions (she must visit her sick grandmother)

- Fear of abandonment/rejection

- Depression

If Snow White is selected, then the problems mentioned below can come up for discussions:

- Male - female relationship

- Father - child relationship

- Fear of abandonment (the Prince may die, father is old, the Prince may leave her)

- Conflict between autonomy (getting married) and compliance (father forbids her to get married)

Conflict between growing old and staying young (getting married or to continue living with the dwarves)

CHAPTER 4

Archetypes in Fairy Tales

As a classical homoeopath, it is my job to provide my patients with simple tests and an environment for them to explore how their symbolic or archetypal landscapes translate into something they can understand and use to make their lives more efficient and full of meaning.

Archetype is defined as 'an original model or type after which other similar things are patterned,' or as a prototype or an ideal. Archetypes can also be defined as energies that get their animation from the collective unconscious. Carl Jung is credited with the concept of the collective unconscious. The collective unconscious consists of a virtual library that stores data of a symbolic nature. This virtual library resides not just in the collective psyche but also in the individual psyche where each individual has access to collective symbols, most of which (if not all) are archetypes. The most well known avenue of the archetype, which is accepted in our current culture, is dreams.

The collective unconscious holds the concept of archetypes. An example of identifying an archetype could be if I suggested the word 'Mother' to you. Instantly characteristics of 'Mother' come up in your mind. Of course, the first impression could be of your own mother so that would be one similar characteristic that everyone's experience of the word 'mother' would share. Other shared characteristics of the archetype of mother could be: soft, nurturing, or playful. It is agreed that these characteristics mentioned are in the positive spectrum. Some other collectively shared characteristics more to the negative end of the scale could be: strict, punitive, neglectful, or uncaring. The point of this is that anything that the culture identifies similar characteristics to, becomes animated enough to become an archetype.

Fairy tales are full of archetypal characters. There are always Kings, Queens, a Princess with her Prince Charming, a Dunce or a Fool and of course a Witch or a Troll. If you sit and contemplate each of these characters, you will surely be able to describe each of them with many characteristics. Anyone else would most probably have similar descriptions, especially if they were from your similar cultural background.

Fairy tales, myths, and stories were originally passed down from generation to generation as allegorical explanations about human nature. For example, and very simply, let's take the tale of *Little Red Riding Hood*. It could be said that *Little Red Riding Hood* is an initiation fairy tale where the Mother sends the little girl off on a path that is familiar. But it is the first time she goes alone. Her innocence and light is spotted by a Wolf; how often do we try to protect the innocent feminine from the predatory masculine which we call, wolf-like in nature. The Wolf then hurries to the Grandmother's house. The Wolf eats the Grandmother whole, and then lies awaiting to prey on the innocent young girl. Red Riding Hood meets the challenge of identifying the Wolf dressed up as the Grandmother, (whom the collective characterizes as the wisdom bearer). Then the strong, mature masculine, as the Hunter enters. He kills the Wolf and the Grandmother hops out of the Wolf's body, still whole and very hearty. In the end they all eat the goodies

sent by Red Riding Hood's mother and they all live happily ever after.

This story is an immensely popular fairy tale narrated in many forms and venues to children all over the globe where there is a European influence. Other cultures surely have initiatory stories that show a similar map of the human journey from childhood to adulthood to anyone willing to listen. At one level, it is 'just' a story to capture the child in a listening moment. I remember when this tale was narrated to me for the first time by my kindergarten teacher Mrs Rita Modi, my eyes opened wide. I was totally immersed in the tale. These reactions, which I remember till date are sure signs of an archetypal experience. On a deeper level, I suggest that from the first time I heard this tale, I started to become aware of the need for me to watch for those 'wolves' out there in the big, bad world. Later, as I grew up and studied human psychology and character development, I realized that every character (or archetype) in the tale is a part of myself. I hold each character (Mother, Red Riding Hood as the heroine and youth, Wolf, Grandmother and Hunter) within my own psyche. This tale, along with all tales that hold such meaning or animation for me, then deepens from a fairy tale about a bunch of imaginary characters, to an inner landscape now made available to my perusal.

CHAPTER 5

Symbolism in Fairy Tales

Symbolism is an essential part of any fairy tale. Common symbols like the King and Queen's waiting are one of the symbols of the wait for sexual fulfillment.

In several of Grimm's tales, Bettelheim sees frogs and toads as symbols of sex. Let's take for example, the famous story by Grimm brothers, 'The Princes and the Frog.' In this story, the frog is a metaphor that represents conception. Water is also included in this metaphor. The frog's proclamation is supposed to represent, that wishing alone can cause a pregnancy. While this reasoning is weak, the other symbolic interpretation of this event in the story is even weaker. Some scholars see the proclamation as a manifestation of the King's desire for a daughter but his reluctance to sleep with his wife.

Since the curse is one of the dominant features of the tale, it is reasonable that many psycho-analytical symbolisms have been drawn from it. The most reasonable of these metaphors is that the curse represents new restrictions imposed on a female at puberty. Another fascinating story by Grimm brothers is *'Brier Rose'* which is commonly known as the *'Sleeping Beauty.'* Thirteen, the age of Brier Rose in some of the versions, was traditionally the age when menstruation started, so it can be seen as the beginning of womanhood. This line of thought leads to more symbolisms. The underlying cause for the curse results from the realization that Brier Rose has the potential for becoming an object of desire. Her potential sexuality threatens men and makes women jealous. Because of jealousy, the old/ evil fairy wishes to stop Brier Rose from ever taking her place as a woman and to die before she can experience the 'joys of courting and marriage.'

The curse itself has another intriguing symbolic meaning. It can be interpreted specifically as the onset of menstruation. Bettelheim elaborates on this metaphor. The thirteen fairies represent the thirteen months of the lunar calendar. The twelve that are good also represent the twelve months in the traditional calendar. The thirteenth fairy, since there is no thirteenth month in traditional calendars, represents

menstruation. In addition, since the curse came from an old woman, there is the added significance of the 'curse' being passed from woman to woman and originating with the oldest woman, Eve.

The mitigation of the curse by the last fairy represents the good fairy's idea, and probably the idea of humanity in general, of how wonderful it would be 'to remain a blossoming maiden forever.'   — McGlathery, page 117

Bettelheim builds on his interpretation of the curse as menstruation, in interpreting the prohibition of the King, her Father. The Father does not understand the importance of the curse, menstruation, coming to pass, so he tries to prevent it. Her Mother, the Queen, being a woman herself, understands the curse and it's importance. According to Bettelheim, that is why she is not actively concerned and does

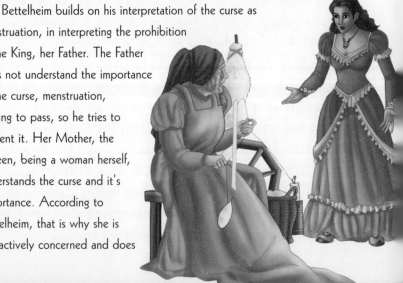

nothing to stop it. The King's actions prove futile, however. Brier Rose pricks her finger anyway. His proclamation might even have served to bring about his daughter's fate. By banning spindles, they become an object of curiosity, so when Brier Rose sees a spindle for the first time, she is drawn to it.

Another analysis suggested other motifs behind the Father's action. By banning spindles, he can prevent Brier Rose from ever having to engage in onerous tasks not 'befitting a princess.' (McGlathery, page 98). The King also takes away Brier Rose's chance to dream, since spinning is associated with dreams.

Steff Bornstein claims that the thorn hedge represents Brier Rose's 'inimical anxiety' about men (McGlathery, page 129). Bettelheim maintains that it prevents sexual encounters before she is ready for them.

Several interpretations see the Prince as a father substitute, since in many versions the Prince arrives in the story only after the Father leaves it. McGlathery goes on to say that the Prince's actions are what the Father would like to do, but is prevented from by incestual taboos.

The Prince's arrival at the appropriate moment marks Brier Rose's sexual awakening and/or the birth of the higher ego, according to Bettelheim. The Prince also makes a 'more appropriate object of curiosity and desire' (McGlathery, page 118) than the spinning wheel which is what fascinated Brier Rose when she fell asleep.

Bettelheim sees two significances in the transformation. The first is that Brier Rose is finally ready for a sexual encounter. The other, which is actually not sexual, is a general life lesson. Do not worry about a seemingly 'impossible problem' (Bettelheim, page 233). When the time is right, it will solve itself.

Bettelheim asserts that how the waking of Brier Rose, perceived by a child, changes as the child matures. First, a child sees it as a coordination of the id, ego and superego. When the child is older, her interpretation will change to the idea of 'achieving harmony with the other' so that two may live 'happily ever after.' This changing view leads the child to realize, preconsciously, that one must be at peace with oneself before reaching out and trying to be happy in a relationship.

If one assumes that the curse is symbolic of menstruation or bleeding during their first sexual intercourse, then Brier Rose's awakening carries a very reassuring connotation. Although this bleeding must be taken seriously, which might be represented by the heroine's hundred year sleep, one should not be frightened of it. It 'does have the happiest consequences.' – (Bettelheim, page 235)

CHAPTER 6

Fairy Tales Interpretation

Of the various types of mythological literature, fairy tales are the simplest and purest expressions of the collective unconscious and thus offer the clearest understanding of the basic patterns of human psyche. Every person or nation has it's own way of experiencing this psychic reality and so a study of the world's fairy tales yields a wealth of insights into the archetypal experiences of human kind.

Perhaps, the foremost authority on the psychological interpretation of fairy tales is Marie-Louise von Franz. In her book, originally published as *'An Introduction to the Interpretation of Fairy Tales'*, she describes the steps involved in analyzing, and illustrates them with a variety of European tales, from *'Beauty and the Beast'* to *'The Robber Bridegroom.'*

In many so-called Jungian attempts at interpretation, one can see a regression to a very personalistic approach. The interpreters judge the hero or heroine to be a normal human ego and his misfortunes to be an image of his neurosis. Because it is natural for a person listening to a fairy tale to identify with the main character, this kind of interpretation is understandable. But such interpreters ignore what Max Lüthi found essential for magical fairy tales, namely, that in contrast to the heroes of adventurous sagas, the heroes or heroines of fairy tales are abstractions that are, in our language, archetypes. Therefore, their fates are not neurotic complications, but rather the expression of the difficulties and dangers given to us by nature. In a personalistic interpretation, the very healing element of an archetypal narrative is nullified. For example, the hero-child is nearly always abandoned in fairy tales. If one then interprets his fate as the neurosis of an abandoned child, one ascribes to it the neurotic family novel of our time. If, however, one leaves it embedded within it's archetypal context, namely, we see that the new God of our time is always to be found in the ignored and deeply unconscious corner of the psyche (the birth of Christ in a stable). If an individual has got to suffer a neurosis as a result of being an abandoned child, he or she is called upon to turn towards the abandoned God within but not to identify with his suffering.

In what follows, my efforts are aimed at interpreting only a few classical stories, or basic types of important fairy tale plots, as it were. This will help clarify for the reader the Jungian method of interpretation, a method which I believe to be well substantiated. If, as a result, some readers feel motivated to try their hand at interpretation and have fun doing so, then the goal of this book will have been achieved.

CHAPTER 7

Women in Fairy Tales

Women in the Western world now-a-days seem to seek images which could define their identity. This search is motivated by a kind of disorientation and a deep uncertainty in modern women. In the West, this uncertainty is due to the fact, as Jung has pointed out, that women have no metaphysical representant in the Christian God-image. Protestantism must accept the blame of being a purely men's religion. Catholicism has at least Virgin Mary as an archetypal representant of femininity, but this feminine archetypal image is incomplete because it encompasses only the sublime and light aspects of the divine feminine principle and therefore does not express the whole feminine principle. While studying fairy tales, I first came across feminine images which seem to me to complement this lack in Christianity. Fairy tales express the creative fantasies of the rural and less educated layers of population. They have the great advantage of being naive (not 'literary') and of having been worked out in collective groups, with the result that they contain purely archetypal material unobscured by personal problems. Until about the seventeenth century, it was the adult population that was interested in fairy tales. Their allocation to the nursery is a late development, which probably has to do with the rejection of the irrational, and development of the rational outlook, so that they came to be regarded as nonsense and old wives' tales and only good enough for children. It is only today that we have rediscovered their immense psychological value.

If we look for feminine archetypal models of behaviour, we at once stumble over the problem that the feminine figures in fairy tales might have been formed by a man, and therefore do not represent a woman's idea of femininity but rather what Jung called the 'anima' that is, man's femininity. Recent studies which concentrated on the question of who the storyteller is have brought to light that popular storytellers are sometimes men and sometimes women. The originator of the tale can therefore be of either sex. A feminine figure in a fairy tale with the whole story circling around it does not necessarily prove that the tale has to do with a woman's psychology. Many long stories regarding the sufferings of a woman have been written by men and are a projection of their anima problem. This is particularly the case in the theme of the rejected woman, who has to go a long way in suffering in order to find the right bridegroom, as, for instance, in the story of Amor and Psyche within the 'Golden Ass' by Apuleius.

Also, in various antique gnostic teachings there appears the figure of Sophia, a feminine personification of divine wisdom, about whom the most amazing stories are told: that she was the youngest daughter of the Godhead, that she wanted to know the unknown Father, called Abyss, and by this bold wish got herself into a lot of trouble and suffering, fell into matter, and begged for redemption. This motif of Sophia lost in matter is not only a theme in late antiquity; it appears also as the idea of the lost Shekhinah in the Jewish kabbalistic tradition. The authors of these religious writings were men. Under such circumstances, we can say that the figure of Sophia represents certain aspects of the man's anima. At other times, however, we could just as well say that the figure represents feminine psychology. The whole problem becomes in one way more, in another less, complicated if we try to concentrate on how the psychology of the feminine and the psychology of the anima are intertwined.

The real woman has an effect upon the anima, and the anima has an effect upon the real woman. A woman has an educative and transforming influence on the man's Eros. A man, especially if very engaged in mental activities, tends to be a little coarse or undifferentiated on the Eros side. He comes home tired, reads his newspaper, watches news on television and then goes to bed (particularly if he is American, Dutch, German, or Swiss). He does not think it necessary to demonstrate any feelings for his wife. He does not see the feminine person and her needs. Here the woman can have a transforming effect. If she can stand for her human rights without animus, and if she has a good relationship with the man she loves, she can tell him things about feminine psychology which will help him to differentiate his feelings. Since the anima of the man will have many characteristics of his mother, his first experience of woman, women in general will have a strong influence in forming and building the man's relationship with his Eros function.

On the other hand, women are influenced by the man's anima projections. For instance, they behave in a certain way and then notice that the man reacts in a bewildered or a shocked manner, because their behaviour does not fit in with his anima image. Even small girls find that if they play the part of their father's anima, put their arms round his neck, etc., they can get a lot out of their father. Fathers' daughters push aside the mother who insist on clean fingernails and going to school. They say 'Daddy' in a charming way and he falls for the trick; thus they learn to use the man's anima by adapting to it. Women who behave in this way we call 'anima women.' Such women simply play the role intimated to them by the man in whom they are at the moment interested. They are conscious of themselves only as mirrors of the man's reaction. Their lover will tell them they are wonderful, but if there is no man around, they feel as if they are nobody. It is only the man's reaction to them which makes them aware of their feminine personality.

Thus, some women give in entirely to the anima projection. A woman I know had very small and rather weak back and ankles, but her husband liked her wearing very high heels. She tortured herself by wearing these shoes, though an orthopedic doctor told her she should not. Such a woman is afraid of losing the man's affection. If he only likes her as an anima figure, she is forced to play the role of the anima. This interaction can be positive or negative, but the woman is very affected by the man's anima figure. This brings us to a very primitive, simple and collective level where we cannot separate the features of anima and real women. Frequently, they are mixed to some extent and react upon each other.

In Christian civilization, as I mentioned, the image of the woman is incompletely represented. As Jung has said, she has no representative in the

Upper Parliament. One could say that the anima is neglected and the real woman is uncertain as to her own essence, her own being, of what she is, or could be. So either she regresses to a primitive instinctive pattern and clings to that which protects her from the projection that civilization exerts on her, or she falls into the animus and builds up a picture of herself to compensate the uncertainty within her. In a matriarchal structure, such as in South India (Andhra Pradesh, Tamil Nadu, Kerala), women have natural confidence in their own womanhood. They know their importance and that they are different from men in a special way, and that this does not imply any inferiority. Therefore they can assert their human existence and being in a natural way.

On a primitive level, the image of the real woman and the image of the anima of man is more or less the same thing. Our civilization underwent certain slow, secular processes of transformation which took about three to four hundred years. This slow movement of development is probably the sum of thousands of individual reactions which, in the course of centuries, have surfaced and suddenly broken out as a movement in time. Possibly the bitterness resulting from being rejected and insufficiently appreciated, experienced by many thousands of women, brought forth the collective outburst of women's emancipation in the early 1900s. It slowly developed in many individuals and then suddenly appeared on the surface so that people became aware of it. Previously reactions had taken place underground. Thus, there are movements which have a psychological background and are the sum of many individual experiences.

We have thus to start with a paradox: feminine figures in fairy tales are neither the pattern of the anima nor of the real woman, but both, because sometimes it is one, and sometimes another. However, it is a fairly good guess to say that some fairy tales illustrate more of the real woman and others more of the man's anima, according to the sex of the last person who wrote down the story, thereby giving it a slightly different nuance. I read in a journal that once, an art teacher, who taught drawing and painting, gave a scene out of the fairy tale entitled 'Faithful John' as a theme for painting. In my view, the story mirrors masculine psychology;

there is only one pale anima figure in it. The teacher gave it to a mixed class of boys and girls, who might choose any scene. All the children were enthusiastic, and the boys naturally chose heroic and dramatic scenes, while the girls picked on the one feminine figure in the tale, identifying with that as the boys identified with the male figures, so that the pictures gave quite different aspects of the story.

Thus, obviously different characteristics are emphasized according to the sex of the person retelling the story. We may therefore make the hypothesis that in some fairy tales the feminine formative influence has been greater, and in others the male, but one can never be sure whether the woman or the anima is represented. A good approach is to interpret the tale both ways. Then it can be seen that some tales, when interpreted from the feminine angle, give a lot of rich material, but from the masculine angle do not seem so revealing.

CHAPTER 8

Archetypes as a Helpful Tool to Understand Patients in Practice

As a homoeopath, it is of prime importance to have a sound knowledge of archetypal analysis to help understand young children and adults', unconscious minds. It is my job to provide my patients with tools and an environment for them to explore how their symbolic or archetypal landscapes translate into something they can understand and use to make their lives more efficient and full of meaning. I do this in many ways. The main tenet I work by is to give validity to the symbolic, and credence, to the unseen and un-rational.

I intend to provide the reader with a working knowledge on how to use archetypal symbology as a tool for self-understanding and to start creating a sense of comfort with the language being used in the world of Intuitive Development.

The most well known avenue of the archetype or symbolism accepted in our current culture is dreams. Psycho-analysis dives into dream interpretation as a matter of course. In dreams, even rubbish can become information which is the language of our subconscious mind and when someone knows the language, it can be translated into information that serves us in a practical, rational sense. For example, it has become customary to interpret water in a dream as something to do with the dreamer's emotional aspect.

Stories and dreams are just two avenues where we can fish for archetypal information. Our ancestors have provided us with other options for use, as archetypal tools. Most of us have at least a cursory familiarity with astrology or tarot cards. Another way is looking at whether you are a Scorpion, Libran, or a Gemini and to recognize these as rich archetypes. For thousands of years, the collective unconscious has assigned characteristics to the astrological signs, houses and even the planets and other heavenly bodies like the sun and the moon. Just from the sheer duration of time, these characteristics take on a rich symbolic meaning. These meanings are valid in the psyche, both on individual and on collective levels. The same applies with the ancient Tarot deck; each of the cards have had characteristics assigned to them for thousands of years which gives them a symbolic and very real experience on a psychic level. Another avenue that has been very popular in recent years is honouring the native American use of animal characteristics in an archetypal way. Generally known as 'totems', these animals and the way they exist within nature are translated into ways we can choose to approach the world. This may be in a 'beauty way' or in a way of 'integrity', integrity with nature and integrity with ourselves.

Another avenue deserves a place in this article. And that is the self. I have found in my studies of intuitive development that each individual is rich in symbolic language. This can be through interpreting everyday items symbolically. For example, a red light means 'stop' or an Indian flag is interpreted into patriotic feelings or a cross makes us think of (and may experience) Christianity. These examples we inarguably share with each other. The self is also a dictionary of more personal symbology. This can vary from judgments we place on those everyday items mentioned above, to items that stem from a familial archetypal dictionary, or very personal associations where no one else shares the animation that emanates from them, for us.

CHAPTER 9

Abusive Conflicts in Fairy Tales

Reading and researching myths and fairy tales provides a wealth of information about the pathways into and out, of abusive situations. Creative thinkers can play with the symbolism in these stories and find new ways to approach their own story. The following fairy tales are from the Grimm brothers, *'Grimm's Tales for Young and Old,'* translated by Ralph Manheim (Anchor Press Doubleday, 1977) and are a good place to start.

- Issues with the father: *Rapunzel, The Girl Without Hands, Rumpelstiltskin, Thousand Furs, Old Rink Rank, Maid Maleen*

- Issues with the mother: *The Three Little Men in the Woods, Mother Holle, Darling Roland, Ashputtle (Cinderella), One-eye, Two-eyes and Three-eyes, Little Brother and Little Sister, Hansel and Gretel, The Lamb and the Fish*

If you wish to explore different ways to interpret the symbolism in stories and fairy tales, I would recommend seeking out the following books: *the Wounded Woman: Healing the Father-Daughter Relationship* (Shambhala, 1983), *On the Way to the Wedding: Transforming the Love Relationship* (Shambhala, 1986), and *Meeting the Madwoman: An Inner Challenge for Feminine Spirit* (Shambhala, 1993), all by Linda Schierse Leonard, PhD; and *Women Who Run with the Wolves: Myths and Stories of the Wild Woman Archetype,* by Clarissa Pinkola Estes, PhD, (Ballantine Books, 1992). Although each of these books explores different areas of life that may be of interest to survivors of abuse, all of them utilize the symbolism in modern and ancient stories to explore the life-affirming pathways and options that have been available to humanity since the beginning of time. All of these books can help you learn how to work with the symbolism in fairy tales (and in your own life), and are wonderful healing tools in themselves.

The myths of the Sumerian Goddess Inanna and the Greek Goddess Persephone are two of the most famous tales of interaction with the shadow side of life, something all survivors experienced. The stories of these two Goddesses can almost be seen as timelines or maps, marking the inevitable downward descent into grief, the most effective approach to healing, and the upward ascent into new life. They can provide guidance and support while you're on your path to healing, helping you see where you've been and what you are left to accomplish. Survivors are encouraged to research these myths and explore the lessons presented there.

To explore the myth of Inanna, a good place to start is the book *'Descent to the Goddess: A Way of Initiation for Women,'* by Sylvia Briton Perera (Inner City Books, 1981). A wonderful exploration of the Goddess Persephone can be found in *'The Goddess Within: A Guide to the Eternal Myths That Shape Women's Lives,'* by Jennifer Barker Woolger and Roger J. Woolger (Ballantine Books, 1987).

CHAPTER 10

Shadows in Fairy Tales

The stories, tales and shows we loved as children often contain clues about the needs we had at that time. We might not have been in touch with our needs on a conscious level, but they were there, nonetheless. Immersing ourselves in particular realms of story and fantasy met some of these needs. You can look at the kinds of stories you loved during childhood to see what those needs might have been.

Some women loved the *Nancy Drew* books. Nancy Drew had no mother but a supportive father who didn't require her to be a proper lady to receive his love. Nancy got into all sorts of adventures, some of them dangerous, and she got herself out of them every time. Can you see the clues here? A little girl who loved Nancy Drew probably felt a lot stronger inside herself than her family allowed her to be. She wanted to be independent and adventurous, with supportive parents capable of seeing her abilities. No matter how victimized such a little girl might have been, Nancy Drew books might have kept her in touch with her highest self.

Some women loved stories about animals or horses. Animals can certainly represent our innocent and instinctual selves, and horses are powerful, beautiful and swift. We could jump on their backs, ride away and no one would be able to stop us! Animal stories are often about how the animal encounters harrowing adventures or mistreatment, with the animal surviving to become free (or back in the arms of a loving caretaker) in the end. It's not hard to see how a traumatized child might cling to the messages in such stories, identifying with the struggles and adventures of the animal. Loving arms to rescue us from our pain might not have been there in real life, but reading about our favourite animal friend's happy ending was certainly better than nothing.

Analyzing our favourite childhood stories can help us understand what our hopes, dreams and secret needs were when we were young. Exploring our childhood through these stories is also a safe way to get back in touch with feelings which are long buried. Since we're exploring beloved stories rather than the abuse itself, the mind will allow important emotions from this time in our lives to arise, perhaps for the first time. For many women, this is an eye-opening exercise; it can be quite a shock to see how your favourite story, long forgotten, fits quite exactly with the circumstances of your childhood, now that you remember the abuse.

Stories From Childhood

- Ask everyone to take a few minutes to remember their favourite story, movie, or television show from childhood (from before they were 10 years old); the one that they couldn't get enough of

- Have each woman tell the group what their favourite story was. Describe the story if others are not familiar with it

- What did you like about it?

- Does this story provide any clues about what you needed?

- Ask the group to offer any insights they might have concerning the needs this story reveals

- How did you get support, strength, information from this story or character?

- Did you internalize any of it's positive qualities?

- Are you still in touch with the positive gifts this story or characters gave you?

- Did you fall short or forget any of these qualities?

- What can you do to reintegrate with this story or character?

- Are there any qualities that you have outgrown?

- Write down any insights about your favourite story, it's meanings and it's implication in your life in your notebook.

Stories From Adult Life

The next step, for those interested in carrying this exercise further, would be to look at the favourite stories of your adult life.

- How do they differ from the stories of your childhood?

- Are the needs revealed in these stories different from the ones in your childhood?

- What are the differences? Are some childhood needs no longer there?

- Are there new needs that were not there as a child?

Exploring the differences in story line, tone and the personalities of the characters can give you clues as to what your consciousness is still working on and what it has handled.

CHAPTER 11

Brothers Grimm's Contribution of Fairy Tales: An Overview

Jacob Ludwig Carl Grimm was born on January 4, 1785 in Hanau, Germany. Just over a year later, on February 24, 1786 his little brother Wilhelm Carl Grimm was born. Their father was a lawyer, and they had six more brothers and one sister.

In 1802, Jacob went to the University of Marburg to study law. As always, his little brother followed him, and entered law school in 1803. During their university years they began to collect folk and fairy tales. Folklores are stories that have been passed down from parents to children, by word of mouth, but at that time many had not been published in books. The Grimm's were especially interested in stories that included Germany and German culture.

Jacob and Wilhelm published their first book of fairy tales, 'Children's and Household Tales' in 1812. The book included 86 folktales. Readers were so happy to see the stories they had been told as children, all collected together, that the book was an instant success. In the next volume – 'Grimm's Fairy Tales', the brothers added 70 more stories. The number of stories went on growing like this for six more editions. Finally, the book contained over 200 stories. It is probably the best known work of German literature. Even if you don't know the Brothers Grimm, you definitely know a Grimm fairy tale.

If only all brothers were as close as the Brothers Grimm. They were always together – even when Wilhelm married his wife Henrietta, Jacob continued to live with them. The Brothers Grimm were both professors and scholars. In fact,

Jacob Grimm is considered to be the father of the study of German history. They both taught as professors in Germany's capital, at the University of Berlin. They became known throughout Europe as experts on anything to do with folktales and German language. They were so into books that they both became librarians as well. During their lifetimes they published many more very important books, including *'German Mythology'*, *'Old German Tales'*, *'The History of the German Language'*, and even the *'German Dictionary.'*

Grimm's fairy tales include stories of kings, magic and talking animals. Even though the stories are sometimes scary, fairy tales allow us to work through our fears. They often teach us a lesson about moral values, and right and wrong.

CHAPTER 12

Oscar Wilde's Contribution: An Overview

Oscar Wilde as an author of fairy tales wrote in a tradition subversively to undermine stereotypical Victorian values. Jack Zipes notes that, 'Wilde was highly disturbed by the way society conditioned and punished young people if they did not conform to the proper rules. He had always been sensitive to the authoritarian schooling and church rigidity which most English children were expected to tolerate.' To Zipes, Wilde's 'purpose' in writing his fairy tales was 'subversion': 'He clearly wanted to subvert the messages conveyed by Hans Christian Andersen's tales, but more importantly, his poetical style recalled the rhythms and language of the Bible in order to counter the stringent Christian code' (Art of Subversion 114). Moreover, Wilde unconsciously created archetypal images that compensated for contemporary psychic imbalance.

Wilde's parents were both collectors of Irish folklore, but his interest in writing fairy tales was no doubt prompted by his becoming a father. He told Richard Le Gallienne: 'It is the duty of every father to write fairy tales for his children' (quoted in Hyde, Oscar Wilde 120). Oscar Wilde's son, Vivian reports that when Wilde grew tired of playing he would keep us (me and my older brother Cyril) quiet by telling us fairy tales, or tales of adventure, of which he had a never-ending supply. He told us all, his own written fairy tales, suitably adapted for our young minds and a great many others as well.

Indeed, Wilde was moved to tears by one of his own stories, *'The Selfish Giant.'* Wilde's gifts as a raconteur are legendary, and probably most of his stories he never put to paper. Richard Ellmann notes that *'The Happy Prince'* originated as a story Wilde told friends on a visit to Cambridge even before Cyril was old enough to listen. The story was "so well received by the Cambridge students that on returning to his room, Wilde wrote it down."

The spontaneity with which Wilde told his tales suggests that they arose, at least in part, from unconscious sources that even he was not aware of.

CHAPTER 13

Understanding Archetypes of Fairy Tales in Homoeopathic Materia Medica

In the evolution of the child, there is always metamorphosis of intellectual faculties. The growing child passes through a series of stages of development, each one of which presents it's own particular set of challenges, which must be confronted in his personal development.

As Catherine Coulter says, 'These archetypal stages of growth and learning are mirrored in the homoeopathic remedies, which are used to assist the child to take in stride the sometimes difficult passages from youth to adulthood.' In the same way, in order to master the psychological problems of growing up, whether it is overcoming narcissistic disappointments, oedipal dilemma, sibling rivalries, peer pressure or letting go of childish dependence – the form and structure of fairy tales suggest images to the child by which he can structure his unconscious and give better direction to his life.

Bruno Bettelheim says in *'The Uses of Enchantment'*, "For a story truly to hold a child's attention, it must amuse him, and arouse his curiosity. Also, it must stimulate his imagination, help him to develop his intellect and clarify his emotions; be in tune with his anxieties and aspirations and give full recognition to his difficulties, while at the same time suggesting solutions."

Every child needs to bring his inner turmoil into order through that which seems tangibly right and therefore meaningful to him. Fairy tales being an important part of everyone's culture, can teach us about the inner problems of the unconscious mind and of solutions to their predicaments.

Telling and re-telling fairy tales to children and adults, educated and uneducated, rich and poor carry important messages to the conscious and the unconscious mind, on whatever level each is functioning at the time.

In most of the fairy tales there is a polarity of evil and angel, or good and bad, or divine on one hand and demonic on other, so when the child listens to the fairy tale he learns to integrate the opposites. Dr Carl Jung in his clinical practice encouraged his patients to talk about their dreams and delusions thereby trying to explore it's symbolic content. The symbolic interpretations help the homoeopath to understand the turmoil of his unconscious mind thereby giving him clues about further management of the case. By bringing unconscious impulses or thoughts into conscious awareness, Dr Jung could really perceive his patients more deeply, and he saw that many symbolic messages that emerge from the unconscious mind turn out to be archetypal in nature. He often worked with these symbols in a constructive way, using a process of amplification (discussing connections with myths, folklore and religion) in order to arrive at an explanation and an enhanced meaning.

Jung also frequently emphasized the process of the balancing of opposites, which is necessary to achieve a healthy integrated psyche. Once two conflicting opposite trends are brought into consciousness, the tension between them can be resolved. A third state, the 'transcendent function' can then emerge. A lack of understanding of what goes on in the unconscious is dangerous, because it means we are unable to confront the 'shadow' and therefore, do not develop the capacity to deal with this evil.

Jung states that every one of us has a darker aspect of our nature, 'Shadow.' It is important in all human relationships, to see and acknowledge our imperfections, which we so often see personified in fairy tales.

Fairy tales is a medium to search for our self, our true nature or what we really are. We all need to transform the negativity in ourselves before we can hope to transform the outer world.

If one studies homoeopathy wisely he will understand that the materia medica, homoeopathic philosophy and Organon of Medicine teach every student of homoeopathy the true purpose of life which in turn helps him overcome his stress, anxiety, phobias and fears; so that he can achieve the higher purpose of existence, showering health and harmony to one and all.

The constitutional remedy is a wonderful tool in this search; prescribing it even in health can help prevent future acute or chronic illnesses. In actual physical, emotional, or mental illness it can help the patient to relinquish the burden of his illness in days or weeks, instead of months or years.

The goal of psychic development (our inner journey) is the discovery of this unique self. The process is what Jung called 'individuation', and it is one of the core concepts of analytical psychology. The evolution of psyche is not linear, but a process of 'circumambulation' (walking around) of the self.

Homoeopaths believe that specific constitutional states (which are also potential illness patterns, since the tendency to illness is 'built in' to physical existence), inclusive of psychological features, are inherent. Psychological patterns, then, are at least to some extent inherent as parts of an overall constitution, notwithstanding the fact that they may also, to varying degrees, be subject to some modification from the environment.

A child's personality is, then, not only structured by parental and environmental influences, but also responds in it's own individual way. A *Bufo rana* or a *Sepia officinalis* child may stoically withdraw, whereas a *Tuberculinum* child will respond with over activity or a *Nux vomica* type with fury or anger respectively.

In the following chapters the archetypes of different characters in fairy tales will be projected along with it's equivalent representation in our homoeopathic drug pictures. In some stories, the information available for each character is somewhat limited; I have shown how they still differ in small but significant details. This is how homoeopathy interacts with psychology – the 'somatopsychic constitutional understanding' (Edward Whitmont).

In almost all the fairy tales of the world there will be an evil wolf, evil jackal, evil stepmother, beast, wicked queen, charming prince, etc. without which, there would be no story. They are the *deus ex machina* (the God in the machine). Their hand is discernable in every event that leads up to the denouement, just as in life, it is our shadow side that contains our weaknesses, and other aspects of our personality that we do not want to admit to having. The ego and the shadow work together as a balancing pair. Jung related the shadow to his intuitive personality. It is this first hidden layer of the personality that is encountered when a person begins psychological analysis.

Fairy tales always have a reasoning of their own, where the wicked characters try to harm the good and the innocent. Here in Jungian language, we can see how a weak ego may be threatened by images from the shadow. This is the most graphic way to understand how we must not let our ego be weak and let the shadow reign in the unconscious mind. However, let me make it clear that shadow is not necessarily all bad. If we face our shadow properly, then it can help us maintain balance between the conscious and the unconscious mind.

In homoeopathy, the 'constitutional remedy' signifies a single homoeopathic medicine which best encompasses the sum total of the individual's physical, emotional and intellectual picture.

According to Catherine Coulter, "The remedies are the building blocks of the homoeopathic discipline, and their pictures remain forever valid." They are, in fact, 'classics' just as the characters in the fairy stories are classics, instantly recognisable, even down the centuries. But like all classics, they must be reinterpreted by succeeding generations. Catherine Coulter uses the word 'portraits' and this is exactly what I will be writing in the next few chapters. Just as a portrait sculptor selects certain features to reveal his subject's true character, so the same is true for the fairy tale figures, and the descriptions of the homoeopathic remedies. Certain features are emphasized, certain themes developed, and certain nuances brought to the fore, because they appear quintessential to the type. Of course the characteristics of various remedies can and do overlap, but in every constitutional type, certain features always stand out.

Many characters in novels of fiction, and fairy tales in particular, portray constitutional types because they are part of our cultural heritage. In real life we see many individuals as 'pure' archetype of a homoeopathic remedy described in homoeopathic materia medica, who may exhibit their characteristics resembling one or at the most two homoeopathic remedies throughout their life but sometimes you will come across complex archetypes who would oscillate between two, three, or four remedy types during the course of their lives, exhibiting their characteristics in alternation.

The figures and events of fairy tales illustrate inner conflicts, they suggest ever so subtly how these conflicts may be solved, and help us to rise in the development towards a higher purpose of existence. The fairy tale is presented in a simple, innocent way where no demands are made on the young mind of the listener. This prevents even the smallest child from feeling he has to act in a certain way, and he is never made to feel inferior. The fairy tale reassures, gives hope for the future and has a happy ending.

This is why Lewis Carroll called it a 'gift of love.'

Fairy tale characters are prototypes, and this is what they have been designed to be. The stories have to be loved for themselves before they will release their secrets. As in the Red Riding Hood, who lies hidden deep within us? And who will come as a wolf in our life? What aspect of us is there in ourselves of her grandmother? Are we dealing with the evil wolf?

I will look at some individual characters from several well known fairy tales, and when it seems relevant, I will expand this to explore the archetype it suggests. Let's begin then. Once upon a time...............

CHAPTER 14

Hansel And Gretel

Once upon a time, on the edge of a great forest, there lived a very poor woodcutter with his second wife and two children, Hansel and Gretel. His second wife often ill-treated the children and was forever nagging the woodcutter. The family had little to eat, and their problems grew worse when a famine struck their land. The man could no longer even get them their daily bread. 'There is not enough food in the house for us all. There are too many mouths to feed. We must get rid of the two brats,' she declared. And she kept on trying to persuade her husband to abandon his children in the forest.

'Take them miles from home, so far that they can never find their way back. Maybe someone will find them and give them a home.' The downcast woodcutter didn't know what to do. Hansel, who, one evening, had overheard his parents' conversation, comforted Gretel.

'Don't worry! If they do leave us in the forest, we'll find the way home,' he said. And slipping out of the house he filled his pockets with little white pebbles, and then went back to bed. All night long, the woodcutter's wife harped on and on at her husband till, at dawn, he led Hansel and Gretel away into the forest. But as they went into the depths of the trees, Hansel dropped a little white pebble here and there on the mossy green ground. At a certain point, the two children found they really were alone; the woodcutter had plucked up enough courage to desert them, had mumbled an excuse and was gone. Night fell but the woodcutter did not return. Gretel began to sob bitterly. Hansel too felt scared but he tried to hide his feelings and comfort his sister. 'Don't cry, trust me! I swear I'll take you home even if Father doesn't come back for us.' Luckily the moon was full that night and Hansel waited till it's cold light filtered through the trees. The moon was shining bright as day, and the white pebbles glittered like new silver coins.

'Now give me your hand!' he said. 'We'll get home safely, you'll see!' The tiny white pebbles gleaming in the moonlight showed the children their way home. They crept through a half-open window, without awakening their parents. Cold, tired but thankful to be home again, they slipped into bed.

Next day, when their stepmother discovered that Hansel and Gretel had returned, she went into a rage. Stifling her anger in front of the children, she locked her bedroom door, reproaching her husband for failing to carry out her orders. The weak woodcutter protested, torn as he was between shame and fear of disobeying his cruel wife. The wicked stepmother kept Hansel and Gretel under lock and key all day with nothing for supper but a sip of water and some hard bread. All night, the husband and wife quarreled, and when dawn came, the woodcutter led the children out into the forest. Hansel, however, had not eaten his bread, and as he walked through the trees, he left a trail of crumbs behind him to mark the way. But the little boy had forgotten about the hungry birds that lived in the forest. When they saw him, they flew along behind and in no time at all, had eaten all the crumbs. Again, with a lame excuse, the woodcutter left his two children by themselves.

'I've left a trail, like last time!' Hansel whispered to Gretel, consolingly. But when night fell, they saw to their horror that all the crumbs had gone. "I'm frightened" wept Gretel bitterly, "I'm cold and hungry and I want to go home!"

"Don't be afraid. I'm here to look after you!" Hansel tried to encourage his sister, but he too shivered when he glimpsed frightening shadows and evil eyes around them in the darkness. All night the two children huddled together for warmth at the foot of a large tree. When dawn broke, they started to wander about the forest, seeking

a path, but all hope soon faded. They were well and truly lost. On they walked and walked, till suddenly they came upon a strange cottage in the middle of a glade.

'This is chocolate!' gasped Hansel as he broke a lump of plaster from the wall. 'And this is icing!' exclaimed Gretel, putting another piece of wall in her mouth. Starving but delighted, the children began to eat pieces of candy broken off the cottage.

'Isn't this delicious?' said Gretel, with her mouth full. She had never tasted anything so nice.

'We'll stay here,' Hansel declared, munching a bit of nougat. Hansel reached up and broke off a little of the roof to see how it tasted, and Gretel went up to the windowpane and nibbled on it. Then a shrill voice called out from inside the house:

'Nibble, nibble, little mouse,

Who is nibbling at my house?'

The children answered:

'It is not I; it is not I;

It is the wind, the child of the sky.'

And they went on eating without stopping. The roof tasted awfully good to Hansel, so he tore off a great big piece of it, and Gretel pushed out a whole round windowpane, and sad down and really enjoyed it.

All at once the door opened, and a woman as old as the hills, leaning on crutches, came creeping out. Hansel and Gretel were so frightened that they dropped what they had in their hands. But the old woman just nodded her head and said, "My dear children, who has brought you here? Come right in and stay with me. No harm will befall you."

But the old woman had only pretended to be so friendly. She was infact a wicked witch who lay in wait for children, and had built the house of bread and sugar just to lure them inside. Witches have red eyes and can't see far, but they have a keen sense of smell, like animals, so they can tell whenever human beings are near. When a child came into her power she would kill it, cook it and eat it. She took both of them by the hand and led them into her little house. Then she set nice food before them — milk and pancakes with sugar, apples and nuts. After that she made two beautiful white beds for them, and Hansel and Gretel lay down in them and thought they were in heaven.

Early in the morning, before the children were awake, she was already up, and when she saw both of them fast asleep and looking so darling, with their rosy fat cheeks, she muttered to herself: "That will be a nice bite!" She then seized Hansel with her shrivelled hands and shut him up in a little cage with a grating in the lid, and locked it; and scream as he would, it didn't help him any. Then she went to Gretel, shook her till she woke up and cried, "Get up, you lazy creature, fetch some water and cook your brother something good. He has to stay in the cage and get fat. As soon as he's fat I'll eat him." Gretel began to cry as if her heart would break, but it was all no use. She had to do what the wicked witch told her to do.

Now the finest food was cooked for poor Hansel, but Gretel got nothing but crab shells. Every morning the old woman would creep out to the cage and cry, "Hansel put your finger out so I can feel whether you are getting fat." But Hansel would put out a bone, and the old woman's eyes were so bad that she couldn't tell that, but thought it was Hansel's finger, and she just couldn't understand why he didn't get fat.

When four weeks had gone by and Hansel still was as thin as ever, she completely lost patience, and was willing to wait no longer. "Come on Gretel, hurry up and get some water! Whether he's fat or thin, tomorrow I'll kill Hansel and cook him."

Oh, how the poor little sister did grieve as she had to get the water, and how the tears ran down her cheeks.

"Light the oven," she told Gretel. 'We're going to have a tasty roasted boy today!' A little later, hungry and impatient, she went on, "Run and see if the oven is hot enough. First we'll bake," said the old woman. "I've already heated the oven and kneaded the dough." She pushed poor Gretel up to the oven, out of which the flames were already shooting up fiercely. "Crawl in," said the witch, "and see whether it's got hot enough for us to put the bread in. And when Gretel was in, she'd close the oven and Gretel would be baked, and then she'd eat her too. But Gretel saw what she was up to, and said: "I don't know how to. How do I get inside?"

"Goose, Goose," cried the witch angrily, 'the oven is big enough – why, look, I can even get in myself,' and she scrambled up and stuck her head in the oven. Just then Gretel gave her a tremendous push, so that she fell right in, and Gretel shut the door and fastened the bolt. Oh, then she began to howl in the most dreadful way imaginable, but Gretel ran away, and the wicked witch was burned to death miserably.

Gretel ran to set her brother free as fast as she could. She opened the cage and cried, "Hansel, we are saved! The old witch is dead!" Hansel sprang out like a bird from it's cage when the door was opened. How they rejoiced. They threw their arms around each other's necks, danced around and kissed each other! Since there wasn't anything to fear, they went inside the witch's house. They ate some more of the house, until they discovered amongst the witch's belongings, a huge chocolate egg. Inside the egg was a casket of gold coins and precious stones. "These are better than pebbles" said Hansel, and stuck as many in his pocket as he could.'The witch is now burnt to cinder," said Hansel, "so we'll take this treasure with us."

They filled a large basket with food, stuffed the precious stones and coins in their pockets and set off into the forest to search for the way home. This time, luck was with them. A little white duck came to their aid as they tried to cross a wide lake. The little white duck carried them, one by one, safely, to the other side. Pretty soon they came to a wood that kept looking more and more familiar, and at last, in the distance they saw their father's house. They started to run, burst into the living room and threw themselves in their father's arms. Since he had left the children in the forest, he had not had a single happy hour. Their father said, weeping, "Your stepmother is dead. You are with me now, my dear children." The two children hugged the woodcutter. Gretel shook out her apron, and pearls and precious stones rolled all over the room, and Hansel threw down out of his pocket one handful after another of gold coins.

"Look, Father! We're rich now . . . You'll never have to chop wood again and we'll never be hungry again." And they all lived together happily ever after.

Homoeopathic Interpretation

The story of *Hansel and Gretel* is one of the oldest contributions of Grimm brothers about two centuries back, but it became really famous in 1893 when the composer Engelbert Humperdinck decided to turn it into an opera. Let's examine the important characters in the story. The most important character in the whole story is the Mother. What are her attributes?? She is awful, domineering and indifferent towards her children, nagging and powerful, selfish, strong, hardhearted, wicked, nasty, and the main culprit responsible for abandoning the children. The Father is weak willed, helpless, a coward, suppressed by his wife, etc. The children, Hansel and Gretel are the true heroes of the story. They have the following attributes — deep sense of anxiety, disappointment, feeling of being orphaned, being deceived by the one on whom they are emotionally dependent, unloved, forsaken, strong sense of frustration as their shrewd stepmother becomes successful in getting rid of them from the house and their own father couldn't do anything about that, thus remaining an ineffective spineless figure in the story.

The chocolate candy house in this story is the symbol of a mother whose main duty is to nurse and nurture her own children so as to gratify their oral satisfaction. Here we see in the story that Hansel and Gretel were quite gluttony, clearly indicating lack of love due to desertion by their parents.

Hansel and Gretel

The following symptoms of Hansel and Gretel were collected and transformed into reportorial language:

MIND - AILMENTS FROM - abused; after being
MIND - AILMENTS FROM - betrayed; from being
MIND - DELUSIONS - betrayed; that she is
MIND - AILMENTS FROM - fright
MIND - AILMENTS FROM - unhappiness
MIND - AILMENTS FROM - violence
MIND - ALERT
MIND - ANXIETY – future; about
MIND - ANXIETY - night - children; in
MIND - DELUSIONS - alone, being - wilderness; alone in a
MIND - DELUSIONS – danger; impression of
MIND - DELUSIONS - deceived; being
MIND - DELUSIONS - devil - sees
MIND - DELUSIONS – doomed; being
MIND - DELUSIONS - forsaken; is
MIND - ESCAPE, attempts to
MIND - FEAR – alone; of being - darkness; in the
MIND - FEAR – alone; of being - night
MIND - FEAR – danger; of impending
MIND - FEAR - dark; of
MIND - FEAR - eaten; of being
MIND - FEAR – ghosts; of
MIND - FEAR – murdered; of being
MIND - FEAR - roasted; to be
MIND - FEAR - terror
MIND - FORSAKEN feeling

MIND - HELPLESSNESS; feeling of
MIND - IMPRESSIONABLE
MIND - INTELLIGENT
MIND - NAIVE
MIND - NAIVE — intelligent; but very
MIND - SADNESS — darkness; in
MIND - SADNESS - fear - from
GENERALS - FOOD and DRINKS - sugar - desire
GENERALS - FOOD and DRINKS - sweets - desire

The remedy I have chosen for Hansel and Gretel is *Stramonium*. They seemed to me quite helpless, with an impression of danger. They feel abandoned, forsaken, left in a terrifying place alone in the wilderness. Facing the sudden realization of this terrifying situation, they feel alone, lost and they try to escape from this situation. They are without support; all they want is a safe and secure place.

The nature of *Stramonium* children is sensitive and a vulnerable one, as reflected in a variety of fears and anxieties which Hansel and Gretel are subjected to, such as the dark (the forest at night) and being away from home. *Stramoniums* are lovable but naïve associated with intelligence, and, again, they show this naivety by returning home after they have been deliberately rejected.

The witch's evil intentions make the children realize that they cannot simply depend on their mother, instead of themselves, for their survival. To do this, they must develop initiative, which indeed they do: Hansel pushes a chicken bone through the bars of his cage to fool the short-sighted witch into thinking he is not yet fat enough; Gretel pretends she cannot work out how to get into the oven (ostensibly to see how hot it is), and then quickly pushes the witch in when she demonstrates herself. They have realized by this time that their only recourse is intelligent planning and acting. As Bettelheim says, "They must exchange subservience to the pressures of the id for acting in accordance with the ego."

Hansel and Gretel's experience at the witch's cottage, completely removed their oral fixations. *Stramonium* is a very important remedy in my practice for fearlessness, audacity and courageousness. When the children returned home from the witch's cottage, they came out victorious, strong, confident and as matured individuals.

The story of Hansel and Gretel teaches us how close cooperation between brother and sister helps them rescue each other and succeed because of their combined efforts. The tale directs the child towards overcoming his immature dependence on his parents, and reaching for the next higher stage of development: enjoying the support of those his own age.

Stepmother

The stepmother is the most hostile force in this story; she is the spark of the story from where the fire emerges of the future events. The following are the rubrics of the stepmother which I feel are the most apt.

MIND - AVERSION - children, to
MIND - COMPLAINING
MIND - CRUELTY
MIND - DICTATORIAL
MIND - HARDHEARTED
MIND - INDIFFERENCE - children; towards - mother towards her children; indifference of
MIND - MALICIOUS
MIND - NAGGING
MIND - NEGLECTING – children; her
MIND - SELFISHNESS
MIND - STRIKING - children; striking one's own
MIND - TORMENTING - others

Homoeopathically, she is *Platinum metallicum,* the mother who becomes indifferent to her children. *Platinum metallicum* is listed in the repertory under 'complaining', and this she certainly does: "...the woman would not listen to a word he said, she only scolded and reproached him." An aspect of *Platinum's metallicum* discontent, which again would fit with the behaviour of the stepmother, is her extreme intolerance of contradiction.

Father

I know many fairy tales where the father is usually absent, impotent, spineless, weak or easily manipulated by giving hardships and ill-treatment to his own children such as Snow White, Cinderella and Rapunzel. In Rapunzel the father agreed to give the baby to the witch in exchange for the rampion he was caught stealing, in *Little Women* and *The Children of the New Forest,* the father is off at wars; in *Peter Pan* and *Mary Poppins* he is there, but severely handicapped or incapable, prone to develop spells of rage and then expiating them with pointless acts of self-abasement.

The rubrics I will use for such fathers will be:

MIND - COMPLY to the wishes of others; feeling obliged to
MIND - COWARDICE
MIND - DELUSIONS - performing - pressured by those about him to perform
MIND - DUTY - no sense of duty
MIND - IRRESOLUTION
MIND - MILDNESS
MIND - SERVILE
MIND - SPINELESS
MIND - TIMIDITY
MIND - WEAK CHARACTER
MIND - WILL - weakness of
MIND - YIELDING disposition

From the materia medica point of view I will think of *Lycopodium clavatum*. I think this remedy is best suited to some of the fairy tale fathers mentioned above, who display typical lack of self-confidence, are cowardice and have a poor estimation of their own mental strength. They are selfish to an extent that they don't risk their own relations with people on whom they are dependent, hence they are extremely self-protective. Sometimes they do realize their inadequacies, but they are helpless as they cannot change their basic nature.

Bailey categorises *Lycopodium clavatum's* in the following way: about half the type are what he calls the 'average Lycopodium clavatum', a quarter are 'wimps', displaying undisguised nervousness, and a quarter are 'strutters', who hide their fear behind bravado. . . all of them are cowards. In *Synthesis Repertory*, under Mind chapter we see the following rubrics of *Lycopodium clavatum* which do fit with this idea of the ineffectual father: 'Fear of children', 'Flies from own children', 'Escape attempts from family and children', 'Forsakes his own children', 'Children, dislikes her own', 'Indifference to her children', as well as plenty of rubrics to do with their cowardice, and confusion of mind.

In *'Hansel and Gretel'*, as in most fairy tales, the father is an inert or ineffectual figure in the background. This is, in fact, as most fathers would appear to the child during their early life, when the mother is all-important (nowadays this would also hold true, but is far less pronounced since most of the mothers are now working). The mother, who nurses the child (especially while breastfeeding), is literally the child's life support system. This is why it is important since she is seen as the source of all food, but here in this story the mother wants to abandon her children in the forest. Platinum metallicum often manifests as a chronically selfish person, which again is exactly like the children's stepmother in the fairy tale. There is a constant insistence on her needs: "We have eaten everything except half a loaf, and then we'll have nothing left. The children must go away, etc."

When the children begin eating the chocolates and candy, they felt in their unconscious mind an image of a good mother, who offers her body as a source of nourishment. According to Bettelheim, "It is the original all-giving mother, whom every child hopes to find again later somewhere out in the world, when his own mother begins to make demands and to impose restrictions."

In contrast to this, the father seems small; his role reduced to that of the absent breadwinner. Such fathers as were present then are not inspiring role models.

Well, so far as the child is concerned, as an infant, the mother and her attitude to him is a 'given', it is only when he begins to relate to the father that he can feel himself as a person, as a significant and meaningful partner in a human relation. This is because one only becomes a person when one defines oneself against another person. And because the child usually sees the mother as an extension of himself, this other person is, the father.

A weak father is of little use to Hansel and Gretel. The frequent appearance of such figures in fairy tales, suggests that, wife dominated husbands are not exactly new to this world. More to the point, it is such fathers who either create unmanageable difficulties in the child, or fail to help him solve his difficulties.

This is another example of the important messages fairy tales contain for parents.

In the typical nuclear family setting, it is the father's duty to protect the child against the dangers of the outside world. Therefore, if the mother fails the child in fairy tales, the child's very life is in jeopardy, as happens in Hansel and Gretel when the mother insists that the children must be gotten rid of. If the father is negligent in his duty, then the child's life is directly endangered.

Witch

Witch here is a symbol of fear, maliciousness, terror and evil. Pushing the witch into the oven by Gretel helps her to lose her fear of evil. She is evil personified, having no compassion or compunction at all.

I looked for the following rubrics in the repertory:

MIND - ATTACK others; desire to
MIND - BRUTALITY
MIND - CRUELTY
MIND - DECEITFUL
MIND - HARDHEARTED
MIND - MALICIOUS
MIND - MANIPULATIVE
MIND - MORAL FEELING; want of
MIND - PERFIDIOUS
MIND - SENSITIVE - want of sensitiveness
MIND - UNFEELING
MIND - UNSYMPATHETIC
MIND - WICKED disposition

I came to the conclusion that the witch needs the remedy *Anacardium Orientale*. She is hard-hearted to the point where she wants to eat the children, and keeps Hansel in a cage to fatten him up, while making Gretel clean her house - thus subjecting them to a prior knowledge of their fate. Dr Edward Withmonth says of this remedy: "They are people who are hard-hearted; want of moral feeling; godless; want of religious feeling;" anger from contradiction   – can kill or murder on smallest cause. Another symptom which I found interesting is 'Weak Vision' since the witch, we are told, is short-sighted. This is, indeed, how Hansel manages to gain the upper hand. She cannot actually see whether he is getting fatter.

I can also see shades of *Tarentula hispanica* in the witch because to begin with the witch seems nice and kind, as 'she took them both by the hand and led them into her little house', but the following morning comes the shocking awakening for the children: the evil face only pretended to be kind; she was in reality a masked wicked personality.

Cases for the Story of Hansel and Gretel

Case 1

I had a case of a child studying in grade 5 who was to some extent mentally handicapped. His mother came to consult me for his abnormal behaviour and other socially related problems. The child was constantly making foolish gestures, was disobedient, mischievous and when provoked by other children, he would get abusive.

The child had a strong fear of darkness and he always needed company. Sometimes when his teachers would ask him a question he would either answer incorrectly or irrelevantly. The child was very good at story telling. He would create his own stories, most of which revolved around witches and other evil creatures. When he would read about these evil creatures and stories about witches and all sorts of violence, he would be very fascinated and his mood would become good and cheerful. But, later the child developed fears and phobias of those very same things. There were instances when he would beat another person without any remorse. The child clenches his teeth all the time, plays with his genitals and even masturbates.

His mother during her pregnancy had a lot of anger towards her husband due to his unsupportive nature throughout. Even through labour there was no support from her in-laws as well as from her husband. Thus, she felt very rejected and full of hatred as far as her husband was concerned.

Based on his attraction for witches, evils and demons and the other mental symptoms, *Stramonium* was selected and given in 30, 200 and 1M potencies. Over a period of six months the child improved beautifully.

Case 2

This is a case of a 7 year old child who presented with bedwetting and awkwardness. Many homoeopathic treatments were given without any result. Due to this awkwardness, the child had a lot of injuries because he would miss a step while ascending or descending the stairs or he would keep tripping. Even while handling stationary, his pens and pencils would keep falling down.

He had nightmares during sleep; he would sleep in a genupectoral position. He was extremely fascinated while reading fairy tales and the one which impressed him the most was *Hansel and Gretel*. He would always pity Hansel and Gretel and wish he could have played a role in the story by helping them get out of the witches house.

The child had a strong desire for buttermilk and cold drinks. Whenever there was any reprimand from the parent's side, the child would urinate more on those days. Based on this history *Stramonium* was given in 200 and 1M potencies. Over a period of three months the bedwetting stopped completely.

Case 3

A 5 years old child with recurrent boils came to my clinic. His other complaint was that he had stammering speech. He comes from a middle class family where the mother is extremely dominating and the father is very weak, spineless and an incapable individual. The child observes this incapable nature of his father and thus develops a strong aversion towards him. At the same time, he is afraid of his mother.

On observation, I saw that, the child was constantly lapping and smacking his tongue towards the lips. He was quite timid, mild with a poor self-confidence and a coward. In school, his classmates would beat him up but he would never respond or revert back.

He had a past history of atopic eczema and his X-ray of the nasopharynx showed a large adenoid.

He was also very fond of reading fairy tales books. What impressed him the most was the story of *Hansel and Gretel*. On further inquiry we found out what angered him most in the story was the fact that the father leaves his two children in the forest. In fact, in reality too, he had a lot of anger against his own father due to his coward nature.

Based on this correlation, I prescribed *Lycopodium clavatum* to the child in 200 and 1M potencies for the next one year. Stammering of speech improved a lot, his adenoids regressed completely and his lapping and smacking of the tongue was also much better.

CHAPTER 15

Rumpelstiltskin

Once there was a Miller who lived in a small village. He was poor, but God gifted him with a beautiful daughter. Once the King happened to be visiting his village and 'in order to give himself an air of importance' he boasted that his daughter could spin straw into gold.

The King told the Miller, "That is an art which pleases me well. If your daughter is as clever as you say, bring her tomorrow to my palace, and I will put her to the test."

And when the girl was brought to him he took her into a room which was quite full of straw, gave her a spinning wheel and a reel, and said, "Now set to work, and if by tomorrow early morning you have not spun this straw into gold, you must die."

There upon he locked the room, and left her in it alone. So there sat the poor miller's daughter, having no idea what so ever how straw could be spun into gold. She grew more and more frightened, until at last she began to weep.

But all at once the door opened, and in came a little man, and said, "Good evening, mistress miller, why are you crying so?"

"Alas," answered the girl, "I have to spin straw into gold, and I do not know how to do it."

"What will you give me," said the manikin, "if I do it for you?"

"My necklace," said the girl.

The little man took the necklace, seated himself in front of the wheel, and whirr, whirr, whirr, three turns, and the reel was full. Then he put another on, and whirr, whirr, whirr, three times round, and the second was full too. And so it went on until the morning, when all the straw was spun, and all the reels were full of gold.

By daybreak the King was already there, and when he saw the gold he was astonished and delighted, but his heart became only greedier. He had the Miller's daughter taken into another room full of straw, which was much larger, and commanded her to spin that too within one night if she valued her life. The girl knew not how to help herself, and was crying, when the door opened again, and the little man appeared, and said, "What will you give me if I spin that straw into gold for you?"

"The ring on my finger," answered the girl.

The little man took the ring, again began to turn the wheel, and by morning had spun all the straw into glittering gold.

The King rejoiced beyond measure at the sight, but still he had not gold enough, and he had the miller's daughter taken into a still larger room full of straw, and said, 'You must spin this, too, in the course of this night, and if you succeed, you shall be my wife.'

Even if she be a Miller's daughter, thought he, I could not find a richer wife in the whole world.

When the girl was alone the manikin came again for the third time, and said, "What will you give me if I spin the straw for you this time also?"

"I have nothing left that I could give," answered the girl.

"Then promise me, if you should become queen, to give me your first child."

Who knows whether that will ever happen, thought the Miller's daughter, and, not knowing how else to help herself in this strait, she promised the manikin what he wanted, and for that he once more spun the straw into gold.

And when the King came in the morning, and found all as he had wished, he took her in marriage, and the pretty Miller's daughter became a queen.

A year thereafter, she brought a beautiful child into this world. Meanwhile, she had completely forgotten about the manikin. One fine day all of a sudden he appeared in her room, and said, 'Now give me what you promised.'

The Queen was horror-struck, and offered the manikin all the riches of the kingdom if he would leave her the child. But the manikin said, "No, something alive is dearer to me than all the treasures in the world."

Then the queen began to lament and cry, so that the manikin pitied her.

"I will give you three days, time," said he, "if by that time you find out my name, then only shall you keep your child."

The Queen pondered the entire night of all the names that she had ever heard. She also sent a messenger over the country to inquire, far and wide, for any other names that there might be. When the manikin came the next day, she began with Caspar, Melchior, Balthazar, and said all the names she knew, one after another, but to everyone the little man said, "That is not my name."

On the second day she had inquiries made in the neighbourhood as to the names of the people there, and she repeated to the manikin the most uncommon and curious names. Perhaps your name is Shortribs, or Sheepshanks, or Laceleg, but he always answered, "That is not my name."

On the third day the messenger came back again, and said, "I have not been able to find a single new name, but as I came to a high mountain at the end of the forest, where the fox and the hare bid each other good night, there I saw a little house, and before the house a fire was burning, and round about the fire quite a ridiculous little man was jumping, he hopped upon one leg, and shouted - 'Today I bake, tomorrow brew, the next I'll have the young queen's child. Ha, glad am I that no one knew that Rumpelstiltskin I am styled."

You can imagine how glad the Queen was when she heard the name. And when soon afterwards the little man came in, and asked, "Now, mistress Queen, what is my name?"

At first she said, "Is your name Conrad?"

"No."

"Is your name Harry?"

"No."

"Perhaps your name is Rumpelstiltskin?"

"The devil has told you that, the devil has told you that," cried the little man, and in his anger he plunged his right foot so deep into the earth that his whole leg went in, and then in rage he pulled at his left leg so hard with both hands that he tore himself into two.

Homoeopathic Interpretation

This story of little manikin Rumpelstiltskin, which the Grimm brothers heard in Germany, is as old as the fifteenth century.

In a nutshell I will summarise the essence of the story — the character Rumpelstiltskin is eccentric. He is clever enough to strike a bargain with the miller's daughter —that he will spin the straw into gold, if she gives him her necklace. When, on the second night the same thing happens, but in a larger room full of more straw, he asks for her ring in exchange for his good turn; but on the third night he starts to take an even more evil character altogether, when he asks for the girl's first child, when she becomes Queen.

When Rumpelstiltskin visits the Queen again after the birth of her child, he expects her to honour her promise. He does relent when she, bursts into tears and pleads with him. If she can discover his name, he says, she can keep her child, since he is confident that the queen can never find out his peculiar, queer, rare name.

Just in the nick of time, the Queen manages to get his name, thanks to the Queen's messenger. Rumpelstiltskin goes into a fit of rage, there by stamping his right foot into the ground, so deep that he sank up to his waist. Then, in his passion, he seized his left leg with both hands, and tore himself asunder in the middle. So Rumpelstiltskin, in the true fairy tale fashion, had a rather gruesome and shocking end, but no more than was his due. He had attempted to tear a family apart, but ended by tearing himself apart.

Having extracted the essence of the tale, it is now easy to select the appropriate rubrics from the repertory.

Miller

The Miller has a very small but a very poignant role to play. He is a typical boaster who bloat's and puff's himself in front of the king who happens to visit his village. It is his stupidity which lands his poor daughter into a life of misery. The real reason for his boasting is to seek importance in front of the king, to show him how talented his daughter is and how proud he is to be her father.

The rubrics I have taken for the Miller are:

MIND - BOASTER
MIND - HAUGHTY
MIND - DELUSIONS - enlarged - tall; he is very
MIND - DELUSIONS - great person; is a
MIND - DELUSIONS - proud

Veratrum album is the remedy that I think aptly fits the situation. They are usually clever enough to boast and make others scapegoats for their deeds. At the same time they are good opportunists, who never miss an opportunity to boast, so they can achieve a lot without much effort. At the same time they are very selfish, as in this story we do not see him helping his daughter when she was kept in the Kings palace to spin the straw and also when she was blackmailed by the trickster cum evil manikin.

King

The King we know is greedy and hard-hearted. His greed for gold is to the extent that, he is willing to kill the poor Miller's daughter if she does provide him with any. Once she has 'proved' that she can, and has indeed spun straw into gold, she is then seen as something special (money being all important), so he is willing to give her the highest prize imaginable that is, himself.

Following rubrics in Synthesis Repertory can be indicated for the King:

MIND - GREED, cupidity
MIND - DESIRES - full of desires - more than she needs
MIND - RICH; to be - desire
MIND - SELFISHNESS

The remedy required by the king is Arsenicum album, as he is self-centred and greedy. They are known to make other people scapegoat's for their own selfish idea's (to spin straw into gold). He was extremely indifferent to the poor girl and her family, as his thinking was that as long as he gets his gold he is not bothered about anyone.

Arsenicum album loves to own the people from whom they get advantage or money. Here the king not only wants the poor girl to spin straw into gold, but also wants to marry her so that he can enslave her for the rest of his life.

Rumpelstiltskin

The rubrics of Rumpelstiltskin that I feel are the most apt are as follows:

MIND - ANGER – violent
MIND - CRUELTY
MIND - DANCING
MIND - ECCENTRICITY
MIND - IMPULSIVE
MIND - INDUSTRIOUS
MIND - MALICIOUS
MIND - MISCHIEVOUS

| MIND - SINGING |
| MIND - STRIKING |
| MIND - SYMPATHETIC |

I feel the remedy which suits him the best is, *Tarentula hispanica*. Rumpelstiltskin is quite a tricky personality; I find in him a great deal of anger. It is this extreme rage that kills him; when Tarentulas are angry, they completely forget themselves in their temper outbursts, acting unaware of the impression they may be making on others. All of this, therefore, matches extremely well with Rumpelstiltskin's extreme reaction to the news when the Queen finds out his name.

The repertory is loaded with rubrics like striking, cruel, vindictive, malicious, etc. where *Tarentula hispanica* is represented very characteristically. Rumpelstiltskin is clever as well as cunning. He does the Miller's daughter a favour in order to get something for him, and in doing so takes advantage of the situation quite cleverly, yet he also takes pity on her when she pleads with him to not take away her child, even though she had promised him earlier. Hence, one sees an element of compassion present in this funny and tricky character.

We also see his industrious nature when, in the past he worked day and night to spin the straw into gold.

In the end, when Rumpelstiltskin was celebrating the success of his dirty plan, he couldn't resist his emotions to sing and dance around the fire, thereby confirming the main trait of *Tarentula hispanica* that is, singing and dancing.

Miller's daughter

Following are the rubrics most apt for Miller's daughter:

MIND - DESPAIR
MIND - DISCOURAGED
MIND - EMOTIONS - suppressed
MIND - GRIEF
MIND - HELPLESSNESS; feeling of
MIND - NAIVE
MIND - SADNESS - despair; with
MIND - SERVILE
MIND - WEEPING - desire to weep
MIND - WEEPING – despair; from
MIND - YIELDING disposition

Carcinosinum is the remedy that I think aptly fits the situation.

The whole situation here is helplessness at every stage, initially when her pompous father announced to the king that his daughter can spin gold from straw and later when she had to be at the mercy of the manikin and his sly nature. What I observed in this story is that the Miller's daughter is completely dominated by her emotions and there is not a trace of intellect. In other words, she is not at all practical, she allows herself to be abused at the hands of the King, and later the manikin.

Instead of reacting to the injustice shown to her, she prefers to sit quietly and weep day and night without a huff. She plays a passive role throughout the story. She allows people to dominate and abuse her, thus making her a victim.

She never intellectualizes, but behaves like a naive individual giving promises to the manikin and giving away everything that is precious to her like her necklace, ring and finally her unborn child. Also she marries the King, despite his nasty behaviour towards her. It is interesting to see that like a typical *Carcinosinum* girl, she does not get angry at the turn of events taking place in her life. She does not argue, or shout or really do anything other than plead, or cry. *Carcinocinum's* are actually obliging and unaggressive. Rumpelstiltskin met his end by succumbing to his own rage, and the daughter did nothing to bring this about. She was lucky that the messenger brought the name to her ears, and genuinely wished to bring the whole matter to an end peacefully. *Carcinosinum* possesses strong peacemaking instincts, and cannot bear upsets of any kind. She is also devoid of false pride, and does not bear grudges. One can imagine how she would have forgiven and forgotten the little man, just as she was willing to marry the man who locked her up in the name of greed.

Cases for the Story of Rumpelstiltskin

Case 1

I had a case of an 8 year old child; his main complaint being severe constipation. The mother feared her child was becoming dependent on purgatives and was becoming worse with every episode; further, the dosage had to be increased with each subsequent phase of constipation.

Without the help of purgatives, the child would pass stool once every 4-5 days, but with purgatives the child was able to pass normal stools. Sometimes, even though the stool was soft, the child had to strain a lot. Occasionally his stools would require mechanical removal. The child perspired all over the body while straining for stool. The stool was black, like black small balls. Any emotional excitement would aggravate the constipation. Sometimes the stools would be very large and knotty.

The child was studying in grade 3. He was extremely selfish. He would never share his toys or his belongings with any of his friends or his younger sister. He would grab things that were given to his sister, even if more than required toys and clothes were given to him. He would still need or ask for more and more. He loved to dance; sometimes when he quarrelled with his friend or his younger sister he would become very angry and try to pull her hair till she would start crying.

He had a thirst for large quantities of cold water; he had a strong fear of doctors and would always throw tantrums whenever he had to see a doctor. He was quite dirty in his habits; he would put his fingers in his mouth without reason. He was a very active child, couldn't sit idle even for a minute; he craves salty and sour food.

While asking about his fascination for story books, he said he was extremely fascinated by the King in the story book and on further questioning he said, "I would want to become a king because kings have a lot of money, power and gold." Then I asked him to identify the King in the story book and he said that he would prefer to be the King in the story of Rumpelstiltskin because in that story the king has a lot of gold.

Based on this I prescribed *Veratrum album* 200 and then 1M, and within a span of about four months I could cure his chronic constipation without the use of purgatives and even without making unnecessary changes in his diet.

Case 2

This is a case of a 10 year old girl who came to my clinic with the complaint of chronic headaches from which she has been suffering for more than two years. These headaches would come very frequently, especially with indigestion. It was a dull ache and sometimes the pain would be hammering in nature. She would ask her mother to press her head very hard; sometimes the pain would become worse and she would start shrieking and weeping. Many times the headache started when she was asleep and she would get up. She was on a regular dose of pain killers. In a month, she would have 2-3 attacks of headaches.

The father of the child had a strong conflict with the mother as he always felt that, she was not the right partner for him. On further inquiry I found that listening to any music would get her excited and nervous, and she would start weeping. She had witnessed many fights between her parents. As a result she had developed a lot of temper-tantrums when her wishes were not fulfilled. She would bang her head or knock it against the wall.

She bit her nails; she was disobedient. She was very possessive and selfish as far as her attitude was concerned. She had an elder sister with whom she did not share a very good relationship. She also suffered from epistaxis, especially from the left nostril. She had a strong desire for cold drinks, lemon and salty food.

She was extremely fascinated with reading story books especially fairy tales. When asked about the characters within the fairy tales, she was highly impressed by the King and the Queen because she says, "These are the people who live in a palace, who have money, who have gold, who have power and one day when I grow old I also want to become a very powerful person."

I gave her various examples from different fairy tales and asked her to choose the character that impressed her the most. She mentioned to me that in the story of Rumpelstiltskin, the character of the King, impressed her a lot as he gets the straw converted into gold. She says he is the one who is very close to her heart because when she grows old she wants to be covered with a lot of gold necklaces and gold ear rings.

Based on this I prescribed the remedy *Tarentula hispanica* for a case of chronic migraine. I prescribed this remedy in 30, 200 and 1M potencies. In a span of about six months I could cure her migraine.

CHAPTER 16

Snow White And The Seven Dwarfs

There is no country in this world where the story of Snow White and the Seven Dwarfs has not been a part of kindergarten curriculum, or there are very few people in this world who would not have heard of who Snow White was. This story was published sometime in the year 1634. In some older version of the story, Snow White was also known as Snowdrop (named after a European flower which is white in colour and it blooms in winter making the other flowers envious of her as the rest of them are withered or shrivelled). Also when Walt Disney production did an animation film on Snow White, they named the female actor, Snowdrop.

Below we narrate Grimm's fairy tale version, translated by Margaret Hunt, language modernized (a bit) by Leanne Guenther:

Once upon a time, long, long ago a King and Queen ruled over a distant land. The Queen was kind and lovely and all the people of the realm adored her. The only sadness in the Queen's life was that she wished for a child but did not have one. One winter day, the Queen was doing some needle work while gazing out her ebony window at the new fallen snow. A bird flew by the window startling the queen and she pricked her finger. A single drop of blood fell on the snow outside her window. As she looked at the blood on the snow she said to herself, "Oh, how I wish that I had a daughter that had skin as white as snow, lips as red as blood, and hair as black as ebony."

Soon after that, the kind Queen got her wish when she gave birth to a baby girl who had skin as white as snow, lips as red as blood and hair as black as ebony. They named the baby princess Snow White, but sadly, the Queen died soon after giving birth to Snow White.

Soon after, the King married a new woman who was beautiful, but also proud and cruel. She had studied dark magic and owned a magic mirror, to which she would daily ask, "Mirror, mirror on the wall, who's the fairest of them all?" The reply was always: "You are, your Majesty," until the dreadful day when she heard it say, "Snow White is the loveliest in the land." The stepmother was furious and wild with jealousy. She began plotting to get rid of her rival. Calling one of her trusted servants, she bribed him with a rich reward to take Snow White into the forest, far away from the Castle. Then, unseen, he was to put her to death. The greedy servant, attracted by the reward, agreed to do this deed, and he led the innocent little girl away. However, when they came to the fatal spot, the man's courage failed him and leaving Snow White sitting beside a tree, he mumbled an excuse and ran off. Snow White was all alone in the forest.

Night came, but the servant did not return. Snow White, alone in the dark forest, began to cry bitterly. She thought she could feel terrible eyes spying on her, and she heard strange sounds and rustlings that made her heart thump. At last, overcome by tiredness, she fell asleep curled under a tree.

Snow White slept fitfully, wakening from time to time with a start and staring into the darkness round her. Several times, she thought she felt something, or somebody touch her as she slept.

At last, dawn awoke the forest to the song of the birds, and Snow White too, awoke. A whole world was stirring to life and the little girl was glad to see how silly her fears had been. However, the thick trees were like a wall around her, and as she tried to find out where she was, she came upon a path. She walked along it, hopefully. On she walked till she came to a clearing. There stood a strange cottage, with a tiny door, tiny windows and a tiny chimney pot. Everything about the cottage was much tinier than it ought to be. Snow White pushed the door open.

"I wonder who lives here?" she said to herself, peeping around the kitchen. "What tiny plates and spoons! There must be seven of them; as the table's laid for seven people." Upstairs was a bedroom with seven neat little beds. Going back to the kitchen, Snow White suddenly got an idea, "I'll make them something to eat. When they come home, they'll be glad to find a meal ready." Towards dusk, seven tiny men marched homewards singing. But when they  opened the door, to their surprise they found a bowl of hot steaming soup on the table, and the whole house spick and span. Upstairs was Snow White, fast asleep on one of the beds. The chief dwarf prodded her gently.

"Who are you?" he asked. Snow White told them her sad story, and tears sprang to the dwarfs' eyes. Then one of them said, as he noisily blew his nose, "Stay here with us."

"Hooray! Hooray!" they cheered, dancing joyfully around the little girl. The dwarfs said to Snow White, "You can live here and tend to the house while we're down in the mine. Don't worry about your stepmother leaving you in the forest. We love you and we'll take care of you!" Snow White gratefully accepted their hospitality, and next morning the dwarfs set off for work. But they warned Snow White not to open the door to strangers.

Meanwhile, the servant had returned to the castle, with the heart of a roe deer. He gave it to the cruel Stepmother, telling her it belonged to Snow White, so that he could claim the reward. Highly pleased, the Stepmother turned again to the magic mirror. But her hopes were dashed, for the mirror replied: "The loveliest in the land is still Snow White, who lives in the seven dwarfs' cottage, down in the forest." The Stepmother was besides herself with rage.

"She must die. She must die," she screamed. Disguising herself as an old peasant woman, she put a poisoned apple with the others in her basket. Then, taking the quickest route into the forest, she crossed the swamp at the edge of the trees. She reached the bank unseen, just as Snow White stood waving goodbye to the seven dwarfs on their way to the mine.

Snow White was in the kitchen when she heard the sound at the door: KNOCK. KNOCK.

"Who's there?" she called suspiciously, remembering the dwarf's advice.

"I'm an old peasant woman selling apples," came the reply.

"I don't need any apples, thank you," she said.

"But they are beautiful apples and ever so juicy!" said the velvety voice from outside the door.

"I'm not supposed to open the door to anyone," said the little girl, who was reluctant to disobey her friends.

"And quite right too. Good girl. If you promised not to open up to strangers, then of course you can't buy. But you are a good girl indeed, and as a reward for being good, I'm going to make you a gift of one of my apples." Without a further thought, Snow White opened the door just a tiny crack, to take the apple. "There! Now isn't that a nice apple?" Snow White bit into the fruit, and as she did, she fell to the ground thus fainting; the effect of the terrible poison left her lifeless instantaneously.

Now chuckling evilly, the wicked Stepmother hurried off. But as she ran back across the swamp, she tripped and fell into the quicksand. No one heard her cries for help, and she disappeared without a trace.

Meanwhile, the dwarfs came out of the mine to find the sky growing dark and stormy. Loud thunder echoed through the valleys and streaks of lightening ripped the sky. Worried about Snow White they ran as quickly as they could down the mountain to the cottage.

There they found Snow White, lying still and lifeless, the poisoned apple by her side. They did their best to bring her around, but it was to no avail.

They wept and wept for a long time. Then they laid her on a bed of rose petals, carried her into the forest and put her in a crystal coffin.

Each day they laid a flower there.

Then one evening, they discovered a strange young man admiring Snow White's lovely face through the glass. After listening to the story, the Prince made a suggestion, "If you allow me to take her to the Castle, I'll call in famous doctors to awaken her from this peculiar sleep. She's so lovely I'd love to kiss her!" He did, and as

though by magic, the Prince's kiss broke the spell. To everyone's astonishment, Snow White opened her eyes. She had amazingly come back to life. Now completely in love with her, the Prince asked Snow White to marry him, and the dwarfs reluctantly had to say good bye to Snow White.

From that day on, Snow White lived happily in a great castle. But from time to time, she was drawn back to visit the little cottage down in the forest.

Homoeopathic Interpretation

Snow White

Now let us examine in the repertory the rubrics of Snow White:

MIND - CONSCIENTIOUS about trifles
MIND - DELUSIONS - injury - about to receive injury; is
MIND - ELEGANCE
MIND - FORSAKEN feeling
MIND - IMPRESSIONABLE
MIND - INDUSTRIOUS - household affairs; in
MIND - INSECURITY; mental
MIND - MILDNESS
MIND - NAIVE
MIND - PRETTY
MIND - SENSITIVE
MIND - TIMIDITY
MIND - YIELDING disposition
SKIN - DISCOLORATION - white
GENERALS - COMPLEXION - fair, blond, light
GENERALS - DELICATE CONSTITUTION

I think that Snow White's constitutional type is *Silicea terra*. It is a remedy with emotional refinement, elegance and beauty, fit for a princess. They have light brown or black hair with delicate and pale facial features.

Silicea terra with the above qualities frequently becomes a victim of jealousy, as can be seen in the case of Snow White who was driven out by her stepmother and was abandoned in the forest.

The fastidious nature of *Silicea terra* is expressed in the story when Snow White tries out all the seven beds, changing them one after another finding one bed too long, another too short, another too hard and another too soft, until finally she falls asleep on the seventh bed.

In this story, Snow White never panics or gets terrorised even when she was left all alone in the wilderness. Her psyche was balanced and stable. *Silicea terra* patients I have seen are always even tempered and sober, as also Snow White who in spite of being so very beautiful never once was proud of her beauty. This is true for *Silicea terra,* as they are never boastful, and will never exert their will too strongly on others.

Snow White enjoys taking good care of the dwarf's in their cottage; for example, cooking, making their beds and washing utensils. She does this very willingly and dutifully, which indicates the conscientious and industrious nature of Snow White.

Self-effacement and imperturbability are the two self- protective mechanisms used by *Silicea terra* patients to overcome their sensitive nature, which cannot easily forget the pain; though it is remembered at the physical level, as the wounds are slow to heal. The common areas of *Silicea terra's* hurt are peer pressure, family disputes, a clash of egos at their work place, etc. This frequently leads to a forsaken feeling.

An almost similar situation is seen in the story of Snow White. Till the time she is with the dwarfs and away from the evil queen and the sinister world, she is very innocent and simple. It is as if 'Delusion, she is born in the new world' or 'Delusion, transferred to another world' or 'Delusion, lives in the world of fantasy with his friend.' Suddenly the Stepmother (queen) comes to know about her existence and then cunningly sets up a plan to kill her by disguising as an old woman and tempting innocent Snow White not once but thrice to eat the poisonous apple and finally when Snow White cannot resist her temptation she becomes a victim of her impressionable nature. This makes the reader learn a lesson that, however tempting it is to run away in search of an ideal, undisturbed existence or trouble-free life, one cannot free oneself from the impact of one's parents and all the feelings around them.

Bettelheim says that, "The readiness with which Snow White repeatedly permits herself to be tempted by the stepmother, despite the warnings of the dwarfs, suggests how close the stepmother's temptations are to Snow White's inner desires." Snow White, we can now see, is a well-developed adolescent, and in line with times past, interested in laces or stays, and having lovely hair. The apple, her final temptation, symbolizes the end of her innocence (as with Eve in the Garden of Eden).

When Snow White lies in her glass coffin, in this world and yet not part of it, she epitomizes the split that *Silicea terra* typically displays: the conflict between the inner and outer life. According to Vermeulen, "The conflict can be between inner life and outer life, again underlining the fact that the *Silicea terra* type lacks the ability to enter fully into life; they are too refined and may themselves to be too special, or too dignified and refined."

In the end, of course, Snow White is rescued by the charming Prince; which indicates that she is now ready for marriage. This further implies that all the stress, conflicts (inner as well as outer) have been resolved and a new personality has emerged. The evil and destructive aspect of our personality (the Stepmother), must then be tamed and brought under our control, which is achieved by the death of the Queen residing in our mind.

Silicea terra may appear serious, sensible and refined and at the same time like Snow White they are friendly, cheerful and simple. In comparison to this, Silicea Arsenicum is also serious but full of anxiety and *Phosphorus* which resembles

Silicea terra very closely is also reserved and dignified but at the same time very fearful and anxious and often lack the intellectual abilities of *Silicea terra*.

Bailey has said of *Silicea terra,* and which I think Snow White epitomizes: "She is neither an escapist nor an opportunist, but once she has dealt with any pressing problem, she will enjoy living with a quiet relish. . . Most *Silicea terra's* delight equally in solitary or meditative pursuits such as art, reading and gentle walks, and in more social activities." *Silicea terra* can allow herself to be herself in company once she feels safe, and then she can be both chatty and playful.

Stepmother

The chief characteristics of the Stepmother are jealousy and resentment, because Snow White is beautiful, pleasing, pretty, fair, fine and enticing. This quality of hers makes the Stepmother jealous every day. The Stepmother's narcissism is demonstrated by her seeking reassurance about her beauty from the magic mirror.

Let me examine now the rubrics of the Stepmother:

MIND - AILMENTS FROM - jealousy
MIND - CRUELTY
MIND - EGOTISM
MIND - ENVY
MIND - HAUGHTY
MIND - JEALOUSY
MIND - JEALOUSY - appreciate anything; desires that others shall not
MIND - JEALOUSY - attention; others getting all
MIND - JEALOUSY – crime; to a
MIND - JEALOUSY - kill; driving to
MIND - JEALOUSY - people around; of

MIND - JEALOUSY - value or appreciate anything, desires that others shall not
MIND - JEALOUSY - women - between
MIND - JEALOUSY - women - in
MIND - MORAL FEELING; want of
MIND - SELF-INDULGENT
MIND - SELFISHNESS

The Stepmother, according to Bettelheim, is 'fixated to a primitive narcissism.' When considering remedies that could match this overpowering jealousy, only *Lachesis mutus* and *Hyoscyamus niger* can come close. The other small remedy I will think of is *Curare*. But for our study I will consider *Lachesis mutus* more than *Hyoscyamus niger*.

Lachesis mutus comes very close in the feeling of jealousy with other remedies like *Pulsatilla pratensis* and *Nux vomica* as they all have issues with anger and resentment.

Lachesis mutus is one of the most jealous and suspicious remedy Hering had to offer to the profession. As Hering describes, *Lachesis mutus* has jealousy that makes a person insane (in the words of Jung 'unlived lives' that is, they can be morbidly jealous of the lives that others are living). They are victims of their imaginations, that others are their enemies and are going to murder and kill them. Sometimes, the jealousy of *Lachesis mutus* is foolish and irresistible as you see in Hollywood, or Bollywood movies, or read in novels and news papers, or see on television.

The jealousy of the Stepmother towards Snow White is associated with rage and a criminal mind. Hence, I will not be reluctant to even think of *Hyoscyamus niger*. I have seen many times in my practice that *Hyoscyamus niger* is extremely jealous not only in matters of love but also of other people's beauty, looks, education and luxury. Most of the wickedness in *Hyoscyamus niger* stems from the delusion that others are going to poison him, or that he is being watched, or he is going to be murdered or injured.

Many *Hyoscyamus niger* patients feel that as they grow old someone younger and attractive will be more beautiful than them (they are very paranoid about their beauty) and slowly they will be overshadowed and not given the same attention (the Stepmother had the same feeling).

Hyoscyamus niger like O. J. Simpson can kill someone; something we commonly call a cold blooded murder. *Stramonium* might do this in violent anger, whereas *Hepar Sulphuris* can only threaten to kill. The other symptoms seen in materia medica of *Hyoscyamus niger* are malicious, desire to attack and kill, quarrelsome due to jealousy, etc.

Bailey says that, "In a *Hyoscyamus niger* individual, the feelings of jealousy can be so powerful that they totally dominate the life of the patient", and this is certainly true in this case.

The Stepmother craves constant reassurance from her mirror, and when this is not forthcoming, she becomes insane with her jealous feelings, to the point that she desires that Snow White should be killed immediately. It is also said of *Hyoscyamus niger* that the individual is very close to insanity, somewhat similar to paranoid psychotic behaviour where no reassurance or explanation can stop him or her from committing an act of violence, as Grimm says, "She trembled and quivered with rage. 'Snowdrop shall die' she said, 'even if it costs me my own life'.

The end of the Stepmother is different in various versions of Snow White. For example, in Walt Disney's version, she falls off a mountain and dies whereas in the German and French versions she goes to the wedding of Snow White and the Prince where she is made to wear a pair of red hot shoes, which makes her dance to her death by the fire which is emitted from the shoe.

The Seven Dwarfs

The interpretation of the symbolism of the dwarfs has to be studied collectively. They were each called by a name by different authors including Walt Disney. The individual names have been given to each of them so that we can individualize each character seperatively. They have been in the past represented as a symbol of good as well as evil; in Snow White for sure they are good. Having said that I feel giving each dwarf a separate name and a distinctive personality, interferes with the unconscious understanding of what they symbolize. According to Bettelheim, they are 'an immature pre-individual form of existence, which Snow White must transcend.'

Let us now see what remedies they represent in our materia medica. We shall first select the following rubrics:

MIND - ACTIVITY - desires activity
MIND - AFFECTIONATE
MIND - AILMENTS FROM - death of loved ones
MIND - BENEVOLENCE
MIND - CRUELTY - seeing or hearing cruelty; cannot bear
MIND - DUTY - too much sense of duty
MIND - GENEROUS; too
MIND - INDUSTRIOUS
MIND - INTELLIGENT
MIND - REPROACHING oneself
MIND - SYMPATHETIC

In this story, the first thing we learn about the dwarfs is that they are miners who travel long distances to mountainous areas and come home after the sun sets. They are industrious, hard working and intelligent in their business of mining, only then can they afford such a lovely home. I have many remedies in my mind like *Calcarea carbonica*, *Aurum metallicum* and *Carcinosinum*, but when I study them closely I feel *Aurum metallicum* suits them the best. One thing I liked the best in this story is that although the dwarfs are immediately impressed by Snow White's beauty, and moved by her tale of misfortune, they make it clear right away that the price of living with them is cooking meals for them and taking care of their house. *Aurum metallicum* is an important remedy of our materia medica where hard work, duty towards ones job and family is an important aspect of their personality. It is listed in the repertory under the rubrics: 'Duty strong sense of, Industrious, Activity desires, Desires creative activity, Busy, etc. Hahnemann said, "He is driven to constant activity, and is sorry for his inaction, although he cannot do anything.'

Aurum metallicum has a strong sense of responsibility at their work place as well as in the family; after adopting Snow White as a family member they leave no stone unturned to take good care of her and give her all detailed instructions on how to protect herself.

I will now discuss some philosophical meanings of dwarfs from history. As the name of Snow White suggests purity, innocence and whiteness, the seven dwarfs in ancient history are described as signifying seven planets that circle around the sun. In the story, the seven dwarfs are workers of the earth, extracting metals. In olden days, seven metals were related to seven planets, for example, gold to the sun, silver to the moon, etc.

There are no female dwarfs, just as all fairies are females. Hence, these tiny, stunted individuals whom we call dwarfs are shown in the story as hardworking miners, who are serious and work oriented. They are miles away from the outside glamorous world that we live in. Hence, *Aurum metallicum* that I suggested for them aptly suits them as *Aurum metallicum* individuals are serious and reserved. They are very independent and totally dedicated. They often don't need anyone's support as in this story, the dwarfs had no contact with the outside world nor before the arrival of Snow White had they employed a maid servant to do their work.

The real character of the dwarfs emerges when Snow White is poisoned by the Stepmother and she dies. The dwarfs take this very badly as a form of guilt, as though they were partly responsible for it. Their attachment to Snow White in such a short time is so immense that they refuse to bury her but instead prepare a glass coffin and keep her body inside so that they can see her. They also guarded the coffin one by one so that no outsider can take it away from them. *Aurum metallicum* has 'Anxiety of conscience, guilty feeling and remorse.' Hahnemann said, "He always thinks he is neglecting something for which he will be reproached." The grieving period that the dwarfs undergo is akin to the brooding melancholy, and delusion that he has neglected his duty; which is so typical of *Aurum metallicum*.

Prince

In Snow White, the Prince has a very small yet symbolically very strong role to play. The Prince rescues Snow White from the glass coffin and enables her to live happily ever after in a time honoured tradition.

I will not be discussing any remedy for the Prince in this story as there is not much to learn. However, the Prince as an archetype requires a discussion.

In many fairy tales they are the main protagonists as in *'The Three Feathers'* and *'The Golden Ball'*, but many times their presence in the story is just to rescue the heroine as in this case and in a lot of the more well known fairy tales, such as *'Sleeping Beauty'*, *'The Little Mermaid'*, *'Cinderella'*, *'Rapunzel'*, etc.

I will now discuss the traits of a fairy tale Prince, which are as follows:

1. Elegant

2. Good looking

3. Impressive

4. Imposing

5. Fearless

6. Courageous

7. Daring

8. Valiant

9. Intrepid

10. Dauntless

11. Dynamic

12. Gallant

13. Faithful

They, the Princes in the fairy tales, are quite romantic and always fall in love at first sight. They usually risk their life to save the heroine of the story. Knowing their attributes symbolically they indicate a man of great deeds something like the modern day Superman or Spiderman. Jung in his book 'Man and his Symbols' says, that the hero, as an archetype 'vanquishes evil in the form of dragons, serpents, monsters, demons and so on...'

Prince as a character in fairy tales is very inspiring simply by their virtue of their rank and dashing personality that seem to make things fall in it's place. For example, Cinderella's stepmother is powerless to keep her stepdaughter in servility once the Prince has claimed her; the wall of thorns just falls away once the Prince arrives at Sleeping Beauty's castle; Snow White miraculously wakes up as the Prince jolts her glass coffin down the hillside.

In some of stories that I know of, like 'The Princess and the Frog', 'Rapunzel', and 'The Beauty and the Beast', the Prince has to perform lots of rescuing and heroic acts so as to keep up the image of their princely dynasty. In Jung's words they must "integrate their feeling side before they can achieve psychic wholeness."

Many Princes have met their beloved Princesses while they were hunting, as in olden days it was considered a royal or a princely hobby. I don't know a single fairy tale which has a Queen or a Princess as a hunter.

Actually speaking, hunters have frequently impressed our young children by their projections. Every child at some stage of life has imagined himself to be a hunter sitting on a white horse and finding a beautiful princess in the middle of the forest. When thinking of people of rank, the child symbolises himself as a source of power and strength; this also reminds them about how powerful their parents or teachers can be.

The hunter is obviously a symbol of protection, in the unconscious. In their dreams, or rather nightmares, every child is threatened and pursued by angry animals, created from their own fear and guilt. So the hunter of fairy tales is not a figure who kills friendly creatures, but one who subdues, and does away with wild, ferocious beasts.

On a deeper level, he also represents the subjugation of the 'animal' within. He tracks down and kills what are seen as lower aspects of man – the wolf for instance – the hunter is an eminently protective figure who can, and does, save us from the dangers of our violent emotions and those of others.

Dr Jan Scholten, in his book on Elements, mentions from the periodic table how the evolution of a child takes place. For example, Carbons, which represent the child, with his search for a quest, in Beryllium he realizes it is all too difficult, but also too late to go back. At Boron he gets help, magical help in the form of spells or beings who advise him. Then he reaches the stage of Graphites, the 'heroic coward' or 'cowardly hero', when he continues doggedly on to accomplish his quest. Nitrogen is when he is swallowed by the whale; that is, he enters a period of difficulties, or suffering and deprivation (as we were discussing above). By Oxygen he is on his way again; with Fluorine he vanquishes the dragon, and with Neon he finally succeeds in finding the princess and, of course, marrying her. This is the finished, inert, stage, according to Scholten. With Silicon he must report back on his adventure...

Cases for the Story of Snow White and the Seven Dwarfs

Case 1

I had a case of a young girl who came to me with the complaint of sinusitis. She also has a tendency to catch cold. When she was six months of age she suffered from an attack of chronic suppurative otitis media for almost four months.

During an attack of sinusitis, she complaints of thick, purulent, yellowish – green, sticky discharge which is occasionally offensive. She starts sneezing as soon as she wakes up in the morning. Associated with the coryza there is a frontal headache and occasional pain in the ear. The attack of sinusitis usually comes on whenever the child is exposed to cold weather or from change of weather or from the draft of an air conditioner. The headache is better by hot application; there is also associated stiffness of the neck muscles with the headache.

What struck me the most was the way she was dressed; so very elegantly. She would always look in the mirror before she left her house. She had to be dressed neatly and tidily and have all her clothes ironed before she left her house.

The child was born with a low weight because the mother had to face a lot of problems during labour. The respiratory rate of the child was getting lower and lower and hence the first few months after birth, the child was in a very delicate state of health.

Academically, the child was very intelligent but she did not have a very good self-confidence. The child comes from a very protective family and she frequently develops a lot of anxiety when anything is expected out of her.

She had various other complaints. Her gums were weak; they would bleed easily. Whenever she was vaccinated she complained of fever, nausea and vomiting. She was slow to learn to walk. She started walking at the age of two years and six months with an unsteady gait.

Thermally, she was a very chilly patient. She would get severe aggravation in cold air, cold weather or in an air conditioned room. She would always like to cover herself up even in Bombay weather (35°C).

When asked about her liking in relation to fairy tales, she said that she was fascinated by the story of Snow White. She said she had read the story more than 200 times and every time she got a chance she would go to her closet, remove the book and start reading it. She would then go into a world of imagination and fantasy. What struck her the most is the character of Snow White. She said she was also very pretty and very sensitive just like her.

Based on this, *Silicea terra* was prescribed in 30 and then 200 potency, and within a span of a few months the sinusitis and recurrent tendency to catch cold was much better.

Case 2

This is the case of a 10 year old child who had a recurrent tendency to develop fever due to viral infections. The child was completely investigated and all the investigations were normal. The parents were worried as to what was the cause of these recurrent infections. Finally, the child was diagnosed to have a poor immune system.

When the child was 4 months old he had developed high fever with convulsions and these convulsions repeated 2 to 3 times within the first year of the child's life. The parents took the child to a neurologist and the neurologist said that this child will most likely develop epilepsy when he grows old. This came as a big shock to his parents and since then the child was never taken to a neurologist but started homoeopathic treatment from different doctors. After homoeopathic treatment was started, the child started developing fever which kept on increasing and couldn't be brought under control with homoeopathic medicines and hence in this condition he was brought to me.

During fever, he complained of dull headaches. Usually the fever comes on during late afternoons and persists till about 7pm in the evening. There was no fixed time for fever but this was the time aggravation which his mother had observed. The child requires a lot of covering during the fever even though there are no chills. His temperature doesn't go too high, the maximum being 99°F to 100°F. Very rarely the fever comes on when the child is fast asleep.

The child is extremely sensitive to antibiotics and cough syrups. Whenever the mother gives him antibiotics, the reaction on the skin is terrible; the child develops severe rashes. He also has a habit of waking up in the middle of the night, shrieking or talking loudly.

When I examined his nails, they were quite brittle and rough. Mother said that the child loves eggs, cold food, cold drinks and ice cream, and has a strong aversion to milk. Every few months the child gets painless diarrhoea. His tonsils were also mildly inflamed. The tongue was coated white. The child had a slightly large head with profuse sweating over the scalp.

I performed toy therapy and the toy that fascinated the child the most was Snow White. On further enquiry, he explained how the story of Snow White co-related with the story of his life. He identified his mother as Snow White because she personified qualities like beauty, innocence, being industrious, etc. He also identified himself with Snow White because of her fastidious nature. He said he would keep his cupboard, his bed, his school bag, his books, etc. very neatly and he would keep his room extremely clean just like Snow White would. He also said that Snow White was a very calm and cool person, who would never develop unnecessary fears and he said this is exactly what he wanted to be when he grew up. He also said that he enjoyed taking care of his younger brother the way Snow White took care of the seven dwarfs.

Based on this, I prescribed Silicea terra 1M in very frequent doses for a period of three months. The fever improved gradually; the child started gaining weight and his appetite improved. I have been observing this child for more than three years now and the fever has never come back again.

CHAPTER 17

Sleeping Beauty

Once upon a time in a far away land, there lived a King and a Queen. They had everything in life except for a daughter, whom they wished

and prayed for everyday. One fine day they were blessed with a beautiful baby daughter. The King, thrilled with the news had a feast prepared and invited all his friends, family and neighbours. He invited the fairies, too, in order that they might be kind and good to the child. There were thirteen of them in his kingdom, but as the King only had twelve golden plates for them to eat from, one of the fairies had to be left out. None of the guests were saddened by this as the thirteenth fairy was known to be cruel and spiteful.

In the end, each of the fairies presented the child with a magic gift. After eleven of the fairies had presented their gifts, the thirteenth fairy suddenly appeared. She was angry and wanted to show her spite for not having been invited to the feast. Without hesitation she called out in a loud voice, "When she is fifteen years old, the Princess shall prick herself with a spindle and shall fall down dead!"

Then without another word, she turned and left the hall. The guests were horrified and the Queen fell to the floor sobbing, but the twelfth fairy, whose wish was still not spoken, quietly stepped forward. Her magic could not remove the curse, but she could soften it so she said, "Nay, your daughter shall not die, but instead shall fall into a deep sleep that will last one hundred years."

The years went by; the little Princess grew up to be the most beautiful girl in the whole kingdom. Her mother was always very careful to keep her away from spindles. Finally, her sixteenth birthday arrived, and the excitement woke her up early in the morning, when no one was around to keep an eye on her. She started roaming around the hallways when she wandered into a room where an old servant was spinning. "What are you doing?" she asked the servant. "I'm spinning. Haven't you seen a spindle before?" "No. Let me see it." Thus the servant handed the girl the spindle and she pricked herself with it and, with a sigh, dropped to the floor.

The terrified old woman hurried to tell the Queen. Beside herself with anguish, the Queen did her best to awaken her daughter but in vain. The court doctors and wizards were called, but there was nothing they could do. The girl could not be wakened from her deep sleep. The twelfth good fairy who managed to get her to escape the worst part of the curse came too and the Queen asked her, "What would awaken her?" "Love," replied the fairy. "If a man of a pure heart was to fall in love with her that would bring her back to life!"

"How can a man fall in love with a sleeping girl?" sobbed the Queen heartbroken. The sleeping Princess was taken to her room and laid on the bed surrounded by garlands of flowers. She was so beautiful, with such a sweet face. The good fairy said to herself, "When she awakens, who is she going to see around her? Strange faces and people she doesn't know? I can never let that happen. It would be too painful for this unfortunate girl."

So the fairy cast a spell; and everyone that lived in the castle — soldiers, ministers, guards, servants, ladies, pages, cooks, maids and knights — all fell into a deep sleep, wherever they were at that very moment.

"Now," thought the fairy, "when the Princess wakes up, they too will awaken, and life will go on from there." And she left the castle, now wrapped in silence.

Round the castle a hedge of Brier roses began to grow up. Every year it grew higher until at last nothing could be seen of the sleeping castle.

There was a legend in the land about the lovely Sleeping Beauty, as the King's daughter was called, and from time to time Princes came and tried to force their way through the hedge and into the castle, but they were all unsuccessful.

Now, it so happened that a Prince arrived in these parts. He was the son of a King of a country close by. Young, handsome and melancholic, he sought in solitude everything he could not find in the company of other men: serenity, sincerity and purity. He too had heard about the legend and was keen on finding Sleeping Beauty. When the Prince approached the Brier hedge it was covered with beautiful large roses. The shrubs made way for him of their own accord and let him pass unharmed. There in front of him stood a castle with high towers.

In the courtyard, the Prince saw the horses and dogs lying asleep. On the roof sat the sleeping doves with their heads tucked under their wings. When he went into the house, the flies were asleep on the walls and the servants asleep in the halls. Near the throne lay the King and Queen, sleeping peacefully beside each other. In the kitchen the cook, the kitchen boy and the kitchen maid all slept with their heads resting on the table.

The Prince went on farther. All was so still that he could hear his own breathing. At last he reached the tower and opened the door into the little room where the Princess was asleep. There she lay, looking so beautiful that he could not take his eyes off her. He bent down and gave her a kiss. As he touched her, Sleeping Beauty opened her eyes and smiled up at him.

Throughout the castle, everyone and everything woke up and looked at each other with astonished eyes. Within the month, the Prince and Sleeping Beauty were married and they lived happily all their lives.

Homoeopathic Interpretation

Sleeping Beauty is a tale that is told, in slightly different versions, all over the world. But the version we know today is certainly hundreds of years old anyway. It is a story that emphasizes that long, quiet concentration on oneself is needed to become a person: "The period of passivity...which permits the budding adolescent not to worry during his inactive period: he learns that things continue to evolve", says Bethlehem.

Sleeping Beauty teaches us how to take life with all it's difficulties and to never get discouraged when things don't shape up the way we want them to. This story is especially apt for those over ambitious parents who throw their ambitions on their kids and push them to become achievers in life. They should learn that patience, dreaming, concentration and quiescence are equally important attributes for the development of a child.

Sleeping Beauty brings out from the ocean of an unconscious mind the theme of sexual maturation. In those times, majority of young girls used to get their menarche at the age of sixteen, which was also the age Sleeping Beauty goes in to a state of deep sleep due to the curse of the evil fairy. The Old Testament clearly states that menstruation is a sort of a curse. Sexual maturity many times in young women is an overwhelming experience where a girl may not be emotionally ready for it. Overcome by the experience, therefore, the princess falls into a long sleep, protected against all suitors — that is, premature sexual encounters — by an impenetrable wall of thorns. It is by this wall that she is often known in some versions of the story: Brier Rose.

In the end, when Sleeping Beauty awakens from the spell by being kissed by the Prince it indicates that now she is ready — mentally, emotionally, physically and sexually to get married. It is like in the language of Brier Rose the thorns suddenly turn in to a bed of roses. The hidden message for everyone who reads the story is that patience and calmness is the key to success in life and that everything happens at the right time in life.

Sleeping Beauty

Now let's understand from the repertory some rubrics of Sleeping Beauty:

MIND - FEMININITY
MIND - PUBERTY; in
MIND - PUBERTY; in - emotional instability on entering
FEMALE GENITALIA/SEX - PUBERTY - ailments at
GENERALS - PUBERTY - delayed puberty

Sleeping Beauty I would say, is constitutionally *Pulsatilla pratensis*. This remedy in all its proposition is a symbol of feminity personified. Dr Didier Grandgeorge says in his book 'Sprit of Homoeopathy', "*Pulsatilla pratensis* is an important remedy at puberty. At that time, the young person revisits the stages of childhood, and whatever has not yet been resolved may now be put in order."

He further adds that, "Every adolescent has to leave his or her parents one day. For *Pulsatilla pratensis*, separation imposed by certain circumstances, is a very difficult experience."

Sleeping Beauty's long spell of sleep may be seen as a metaphor for resolving her inner conflicts. When these conflicting ideas get resolved she awakens from her sleep, now a completely new person ready to enter the new world of womanhood. When we talk of womanhood we also consider menstrual problems which frequently accompany many women during that period; *Pulsatilla pratensis* is an excellent remedy in homoeopathy which covers very well the problems associated with puberty to premenstrual syndrome to dysmenorrhoea, etc.

Sleeping Beauty tries to delay her entry into womanhood by going into a slumber. *Pulsatilla pratensis*, as Dr Dider Grandgeorge puts it, "The umbilical cord has truly not been cut; that means that separation from mother is extremely painful and difficult."

Wicked Fairy

The wicked fairy in this story is portrayed as an extremely jealous character. She projects qualities like envy, insane, jealousy, hard-heartedness just because the King did not invite her, knowing how painful it would be for the King and Queen to see their own daughter die at such a tender age.

Let's examine the rubrics of the Wicked Fairy:

MIND - CRUELTY
MIND - DELUSIONS — insulted; he is
MIND - ENVY
MIND - ENVY - happy; seeing other people
MIND - ENVY - hate, and
MIND - HARDHEARTED
MIND - HATRED - revengeful; hatred and
MIND - JEALOUSY

MIND - JEALOUSY - revenge, wants to take
MIND - MALICIOUS
MIND - RAGE
MIND - SENSITIVE - want of sensitiveness
MIND - UNFEELING
MIND - WICKED disposition

Remedies which come for consideration are *Anacardium orientale, Crocus sativus, Hyoscyamus niger, Lachesis mutus, Platinum metallicum* and *Tarantula hispanica.*

I personally feel the wicked fairy is *Platinum metallicum.* In this case, the fairy felt neglected and insulted because she wasn't invited and as a result her fragile ego gets hurt and she in anger shoots a curse on the young Princess. I have seen in my practise many *Platinum metallicum* patients to be revengeful if they are neglected even for a slightest cause.

Lachesis mutus is another remedy which I would think of because she attacks like a snake the moment she is insulted. *Lachesis mutus* patients are sensitive to insults and have a lot of issues related to ego. Dr Hering says, "The person needs to be acknowledged, even as someone special, and if that does not happen she can be extremely negative and take revenge, behaving maliciously and vindictively. Becomes easily peevish and mistrustful, believes himself intentionally injured by all about him, and attaches the most hateful significance to the most innocent occurrences."

Tarantula hispanica is also sensitive to insults. The effect of this emotional injury is very deep and long lasting. Jealousy in them can lead to anger which can further lead to violent behaviour.

Princess as the Archetype in Fairy Tales

The moment one thinks about a prince and princess the following things come to one's mind, for example, beautiful horses, chariots, large garden with beautiful flowers, huge palace or castles with lots of rooms with beautiful maids, large swimming pool, a pond with swans, nice music that is being played by the musicians, etc. All these indicate a feeling of glamour and hence many of us are attracted to read about kings, queens and royal families. Princesses in fairy tales are usually portrayed as beautiful, pretty, attractive, enticing, graceful, refined, rich, shapely and splendid. Some are even portrayed as fragile, delicate and pure.

They are extraordinary in whatever they do; everything they do is exclusive, miles away from common humdrum existence.

Almost all the princesses of fairy tale are virgin and they eagerly await their turn to hold the arms of a charming prince. Their life is very simple and easy like that of a child and they have nothing much to do except for looking beautiful, singing, dancing, sitting in gardens reading books, etc.

Homoeopathic materia medica has many archetype of princesses namely *Carcinosinum, Pulsatilla pratensis, Silicea terra, Phosphorus;* each one with it's own characteristics. All of them are mild, gentle, fragile, beautiful and perfect.

They all have a very pleasing personality. *Carcinosinum* has a lot of natural ability like *Sepia officinalis* to have a sense of aesthetics. This sense of aesthetics usually attracts princes from far and distant lands to marry them.

A *Silicea terra* princess is more intelligent and highly moralistic as compared to a *Carcinosinum* or *Pulsatila pratensis* princess.

These drugs describe the typical fairy tale princesses mentioned above. However, there is another type of princess found in fairy tales who is not very commonly seen. This princess is rather spoilt, autocratic, fretful, shrewish, sullen, petulant and extremely demanding because she belongs to the aristocratic class. They are proud to be rich, bold and beautiful.

The best example is to study the story written by the Grimm brothers named *'King Thrushbeard'* or Hans Christian Anderson's *'The Swineheard.'* In these stories you will witness princesses with lots of rudeness, tantrums, full of whims and fancies, who go about humiliating and insulting people around them. Now let's have a glimpse at the rubrics of such a princess:

MIND - ABUSIVE
MIND - ABUSIVE - insulting
MIND - ANGER - vex others; inclined to
MIND - CENSORIOUS
MIND - CONTEMPTUOUS
MIND - HAUGHTY
MIND - IMPOLITE
MIND - INSOLENCE
MIND - MALICIOUS - insulting
MIND - QUARRELSOME
MIND - RUDENESS
MIND - TEMPER TANTRUMS

Now if we examine the rubrics carefully, I feel drugs like *Mercurius, Platinum metallicum, Palladium metallicum* and *Lyssinum* will come up for comparison.

Dr Philip Bailey says, "*Mercurius* is a fascinating type. It is probably harder to 'get a handle' on the *Mercurius* personality than on that of any other constitutional type. How do you get a handle on something so multifaceted, so changeable and so contradictory?" he further adds, "The scope of the *Mercurius* personality is truly vast. On the one hand there are immature *Mercurius* youths who are extremely impressionable, flighty and unreliable, and on the other hand mature individuals who have a lot of wisdom and a lot of personal power." Further Vermeulen, in his 'Synoptic Reference' mentions, "Very sensitive to criticism and contradiction; may become violent (desire to kill the person that contradicts her, hatred of persons who had offended him)."

Next in the list is *Platinum metallicum*; here the main theme is pride, sexuality and narcissistic tendency. It's keynotes are hysteria, pride and nymphomania. Like a rude princess she can be very nasty, mean, revengeful and impolite.

Gross in his materia medica mentions the following, "Contemptuous, pitying, looking down on people at other times respected, with a certain disdain..." In *'King Thrush − Beard'*, the princess insults all her beau, by passing nasty remarks and insulting them thoroughly.

Next in the list is *Palladium metallicum*, for which Dr H.C. Allen says, "Strong inclination to use forcible language and violent expressions."

Vermeulen says, "The haughtiness is in the constant need to be included, the constant need to be flattered or paid attention to." They want to be the centre of attraction and are convinced about their own attractiveness.

Cases From the Story of Sleeping Beauty

Case 1

I had a case of an 11 year old girl who came to me with the complaint of recurrent attacks of acne on her face. Her eruptions were aggravated by eating fatty foods, rich foods, butter, ice cream, or whenever she had problems related with her digestion.

She also complained of recurrent sinusitis which was characterised by nasal obstruction, worse in the evening and at night, on lying down and better in the open air. She has a sense of congestion around the paranasal area. She occasionally complained of a thick, offensive and purulent discharge from the nose. She also complained of excessive lachrymation due to over straining of the eyes by continuously reading or working on the computer. As a child, she had a history of recurrent otitis media. Her digestion has always been weak. She loves eggs, sour and fruits. There is mild dribbling of saliva during sleep and she prefers to sleep on her abdomen. Her haemoglobin was checked on two occasions and it came to 10.5 gm% which indicated that she was also anaemic.

Her mother was a school teacher and her father worked in a bank. She was extremely dependant on her parents for everything. Due to her timid nature she was unable to express her feeling even to her own parents. She loves animals; darkness aggravates her in every way; she bites her nails when she is stressed; she is relatively irresolute; otherwise in general, she is quite mild. Her younger brother was born when she was 4 years old and this made her very insecure. It was then that she had her first attack of otitis media.

She was also very fond of reading fairy tales especially the story of *Sleeping Beauty*. She was very impressed by the beauty bestowed by God on this Princess. She said she hated the part when the witch cursed the Princess that she would prick herself with a needle and drop dead when she was fifteen. She said she hates witches and evil characters in fairy tales, so much so that she would prefer to skip those parts in the story.

Based on this, I prescribed *Pulsatilla pratensis* 200 which helped the patient with her acne. She became much more independent as a person after *Pulsatilla pratensis*.

Case 2

This is the case of an 8 year old child who came to me with the complaint of growing pains. She complained of severe pain in the limbs, especially over the muscles of the leg and calf region. The pain was worse in the evening, worse lying down, worse slightest motion or touch and worse in a warm room. She said she felt better if she was in a cold room, or on the application of ice water, or any kind of cold application.

She had complaint of nocturnal enuresis. Mother recited "She wets the bed in the first half of the night. Usually she complains of seeing frightful dreams of ghosts and dark black animals coming to attack her which she feels leads to her bedwetting. She also had a strong fear of darkness. She passes urine quite frequently in cold weather but repeatedly I have confirmed that she passes urine involuntary in the first half of the night. During her sleep, she is quite restless."

When I probed into her family situation, I realised that she was studying in a school where one of her teachers was rather mean to her. She would insult and humiliate the child in front of her classmates, because she felt the child was slightly dyslexic. This led her to withdraw from everything, her level of confidence diminished and it was always a mental stress factor for her.

Her parents also complained that she had a weak memory and was unable to learn her poetry and verses as well as other children her age. She was extremely sensitive to reprimands or rudeness.

She had a past history of measles, mumps and recurrent tonsillitis. She was almost thirstless. Sometimes due to excessive weeping she would get a headache. She had a fair complexion but her face was pale and her lips were dry. She had a strong craving for cheese and cold drinks.

When Jungian toys were shown to her and she was asked to describe the fairy tale which touched her the most, she started talking about Sleeping Beauty. She considered Sleeping Beauty as one of the most beautiful ladies to ever exist and she was extremely thrilled when the Prince came to the kingdom, finds the lost castle, kisses the Princess and the Princess comes back to life. This impressed her so much that she starts weeping at the end of the story.

Based on this I prescribed *Pulsatilla pratensis* 200 and 1M. Within a span of three months her bedwetting and the growing pains were much better.

CHAPTER 18

Little Red Riding Hood

A large number of versions of this story have been traced to the various regions of France (Zipes, 1993). The most popular versions of Little Red Riding Hood or Little Red Cap have been created by Perrault and the Brothers Grimm. However, both recorders have been criticized for making alterations in what was considered to be the original oral text (Dundes, 1989).

Once upon a time, there was a little girl who lived in a village near the forest. Whenever she went out, the little girl wore a red riding cloak, so everyone in the village called her Little Red Riding Hood.

One morning, Little Red Riding Hood asked her mother if she could go to visit her grandmother as it had been awhile since they'd seen each other. "That's a good idea," her mother said. So they packed a nice basket for Little Red Riding Hood to take to her grandmother. When the basket was ready, the little girl put on her red cloak and kissed her mother goodbye.

"Remember, go straight to Grandma's house," her mother cautioned. "Don't dawdle along the way and please don't talk to strangers! The woods are dangerous." "Don't worry, Mommy," said Little Red Riding Hood, "I'll be careful." But when Little Red Riding Hood noticed some lovely flowers in the woods, she forgot her promise to her mother. She picked a few, watched the butterflies flit about for a while, listened to the frogs croaking and then picked a few more.

Little Red Riding Hood was enjoying the warm summer day so much, that she didn't notice a dark shadow approaching out of the forest behind her...

Suddenly, the Wolf appeared beside her.

"What are you doing out here, little girl?" the Wolf asked in a voice as friendly as he could muster.

"I'm on my way to see my Grandma who lives through the forest, near the brook," Little Red Riding Hood replied.

Then she realized how late she was and quickly excused herself, rushing down the path to her Grandma's house.

The Wolf, in the meantime, took a shortcut.

The Wolf, a little out of breath from running, arrived at Grandma's and knocked lightly at the door.

"Oh thank goodness dear! Come in, come in! I was worried sick that something had happened to you in the forest," said Grandma thinking that the knock was her granddaughter.

The Wolf let himself in. Poor Granny did not have time to say another word, before the Wolf gobbled her up.

The Wolf let out a satisfied burp, and then poked through Granny's wardrobe to find a nightgown that he liked. He added a frilly sleeping cap, and for good measure, dabbed some of Granny's perfume behind his pointy ears.

A few minutes later, Red Riding Hood knocked on the door. The Wolf jumped into bed and pulled the covers over his nose. "Who is it?" he called in a cackly voice.

"It's me, Little Red Riding Hood."

"Oh how lovely! Do come in, my dear," croaked the Wolf.

When Little Red Riding Hood entered the little cottage, she could scarcely recognize her Grandmother.

"Grandmother! Your voice sounds so odd. Is something the matter?" she asked.

"Oh, I just have the touch of a cold," squeaked the Wolf adding a cough at the end to prove his point.

"But Grandmother! What big ears you have," said Little Red Riding Hood as she edged closer to the bed. "The better to hear you with, my dear," replied the Wolf.

"But Grandmother! What big eyes you have," said Little Red Riding Hood. "The better to see you with, my dear," replied the Wolf.

"But Grandmother! What big teeth you have," said Little Red Riding Hood her voice quivering slightly. "The better to eat you with, my dear."

And scarcely had the Wolf said this, than with one bound he was out of bed and swallowed up Red Riding Hood.

When the Wolf had appeased his appetite, he lay down again in the bed, fell asleep and began to snore very loud.

The Huntsman was just passing the house, and thought to himself: 'How the old woman is snoring! I must just see if she wants anything.' So he went into the room, and when he came to the bed, he saw that the Wolf was lying in it.

'Do I find you here, you old sinner!' said he. 'I have long sought you!' But just as he was going to fire at him, it occurred to him that the wolf might have devoured the Grandmother, and that she might still be saved, so he did not fire, but took a pair of scissors, and began to cut open the stomach of the sleeping Wolf.

When he had made two snips, he saw Little Red Riding Hood shining, and then he made two snips more, and the little girl sprang out, crying: "Ah, how frightened I have been! How dark it was inside the Wolf."

After that the aged Grandmother came out alive also, but scarcely able to breathe. Red Riding Hood, however, quickly fetched great stones with which they filled the wolf's belly, and when he awoke, he wanted to run away, but the so heavy that he collapsed at once, and fell dead.

Then all three were delighted. The huntsman drew off the Wolf's skin and went home with it; the Grandmother ate the cake and drank the wine which Red Riding Hood had brought, and revived. But Red Riding Hood thought to herself: "As long as I live, I will never leave the path by myself to run into the wood, when my mother has forbidden me to do so." Red Riding Hood went joyously home and no one ever did anything to harm her again.

Psycho-analysis of the Tale

Among the most popular psycho-analytic interpretations regarding this tale are the ones proposed by Fromm (1951), Roheim (1953) and Bettelheim (1976).

Fromm's (1951) interpretation stressed on the significance of the red hood that is said to symbolize menstruation and serves as a signal of her forthcoming femininity. He also interprets this tale as a battle between the two sexes whereby the female attempts to humiliate the male, by placing stones in his stomach (stones are considered to be a symbol of sterility). "It is a story of triumph by men-hating women, ending with their victory."

Alice Miller (1981) challenges the notion of projection regarding violence and aggression in fairy tales. Instead, she argues that some fairy tales are adults' censored projections of abuse that they actually experienced as children.

Bettelheim, of course, is not the only Freudian to read dark sexual meanings into the story. Psychoanalyst Erich Fromm, in The Forgotten Language: An Introduction to the Understanding of Dreams, Fairy Tales, and Myths (1951) is also convinced that LRRH is experiencing unconscious sexual impulses and really wants to be seduced by the wolf. The red cape symbolizes her menstrual blood as she enters womanhood. When the mother warns her not to leave the path or she might fall and break the wine bottle, it represents the mother's fear that her daughter might lose her virginity by breaking her maidenhead.

Little Red Riding Hoods budding sexuality is directed towards the Wolf who is an externalization of the dangers of overwhelming oedipal longings. The father is also portrayed as the Hunter in his protective and rescuing role. Thus, we may observe the splitting of the father figure into a ferocious and threatening animal and into a benign and helpful hunter.

Verena Kast (1995), adopting a Jungian perspective writes that the Wolf symbolizes the instinctive, primitive nature of the heroine. "She meets in the Wolf part of her nature, the part of herself that she has denied: a Red Cap who is dreamy, aggressive, desperate and dangerously greedy in her search for life... As a wolf, she gets to know an aspect of herself that is loose, that doesn't care about duties or about what others think about her."

The story of Little Red Riding Hood reflects the child's anxiety during separation and their fear of annihilation. As the young girl enters the wood she feels anxious about having left the security of her home, the dangers that may lie ahead, it getting dark or her being left alone (being left alone in the house, in some Asian versions).

The most common responses I get for Little Red Riding Hood during the psychoanalysis of my young patients is anxiety over an impending danger or risks that lie ahead.

The figure of the Wolf or the tiger is a symbolic expression of archaic fears (darkness, strangers, solitude) and separation anxiety. The Wolf, as an externalization of separation anxiety and archaic fears may also be observed in other popular tales such as 'The Wolf and the Seven Kids' and 'The Three Little Pigs' whereby the protagonists are temporarily abandoned by their mothers.

Little Red Riding Hood is unable to cope with these fears because of her immature and weak ego, so she redirects them toward her (grand) mother, 'expecting' that she will protect her by dealing with them. In this fairy tale we have the splitting of the mother into a young mother and into an old and disabled (grand) mother. In both cases, the mother urges her daughter to cope with her fears and deal with dangers. At the beginning of the story, she sends her daughter to visit her Grandmother who lives across the wood. She trusts the girl to make it there safely while being aware of the dangers that this walk entails. At the end of the story, as an old, sick woman, she is unable to protect the little girl and she succumbs to the Wolf's cunningness, leaving Little Red Riding Hood alone to cope with her fears and anxieties 'face to face.'

When Little Red Riding Hood enters Grandmother's cottage and sees the Wolf in disguise, she does not recognize him. This refusal or denial may be attributed to her facing the devastating consequences of archaic fears, namely, annihilation (or death).

In Snow White, we have the splitting of the mother probably due to oedipus conflicts into the wicked witch and into the benevolent dwarfs.

Looking at the happy ending of the French oral text as well as the happy ending of the Chinese and Japanese versions, we observe that it is the heroine(s) who saves herself. When the Wolf reveals his intentions, the heroine's ego takes over and she reacts with reason and maturity, thus managing to outwit the Wolf.

The ending in the Grimm's version demonstrates Little Red Riding Hood's inability to deal with her fears and thus she is eventually 'devoured' by them. Still dependent, she expects to be saved by a strong paternal figure.

Having looked at fairy tale villains above, I want to look briefly at the story of Little Red Riding Hood. The villain in this tale is, of course, the big bad Wolf and he has been discussed at length, but what about the heroine? She is an ordinary little girl, every girl as it was…

Little Red Riding Hood v/s Hansel and Gretel

A charming 'innocent' young girl swallowed by a wolf is an image which impresses itself forever on the mind. Unlike Hansel and Gretel (who managed to escape from being eaten), Red Riding Hood and her grandmother are actually eaten and then cut out of the wolf's tummy.

The threat of being devoured is, again, therefore the central theme of the story. Hansel and Gretel deal with their difficulties and anxieties when they are forced to give up their dependent attachment to their mother and according to Bettelheim, 'free himself of his oral fixation.' Little Red Riding Hood focuses on crucial problems children deal with in their schooling age whereby they need to be given adequate exposure of dangerous situations in order to build up their own personality.

While Hansel and Gretel have to be pushed out into the world, Red Riding Hood leaves her home willingly; she is not afraid of the outside world, but recognises its attractions wherein lie it's dangers. Little Red Riding Hood is more mature than Hansel and Gretel, as is shown by her interest towards what she encounters in the world.

Red Riding Hood is universally loved because, although she is virtuous, she is tempted; and because her fate tells us that trusting everybody's good intentions, which seem so nice, is really leaving oneself open to pitfalls.

Rubrics for Little Red Riding Hood are:

MIND - ANXIETY — others; for
MIND - BENEVOLENCE
MIND - CREDULOUS
MIND - EXTROVERTED PERSONALITY
MIND - IMPRESSIONABLE
MIND - NAIVE
MIND - SENSITIVE - external impressions; to all
MIND - SYMPATHETIC

The remedy *Phosphorus* or *Carcinosinum* is the perfect example of Little Red Riding Hood. Basically she is naive, impressionable and innocent. *Phosphorus* is easily distracted — which we see when Little Red Riding Hood strays off the path, even though she had been warned not to do so, to pick flowers. She is totally involved in this diversion, only stopping when she has no space in her arms for more.

Her interaction with the wolf clearly demonstrates her simplicity as seen frequently when one reads a fairy tale.

Phosphorus children according to me are weak and devoid of mental firmness as well as physical energy. Hence, many times they are not stable and drift like a straw in the air; like a helpless victim. It is an outside influence which is generally the root cause of their suffering. Due to their weak will, they find no strength within themselves and look for support in the outside world.

Dr Edward Whitmont says that they are individuals likely to blossom in the 'sunshine' of favourable circumstances, but wilt in adversity.

Catherine Coulter mentions in her *'Portraits of Materia Medica'*: "He appeals by his alluring looks and bright manner, and especially by his sparkling eyes. Even chance passer-bys exclaim 'What a lovely child!'" She says they are light-hearted and ultra-impressionable children, seeking to make people around them happy, since they are highly responsive to others' moods. It is the transparently open child who is likely to be *Phosphorus*.

They are always eager to help out when asked, many times lost in day-dreaming or easily distracted, *'phosphorus'* children forget all about the commitment they had undertaken. So it is with Little Red Riding Hood, as she strays off the path, distracted by the flowers growing in the wood.

Like any other tubercular remedy, *Phosphorus* children search for emotional excitement to ward off the boredom that easily descends on them. It's like young adolescent girls, who may have difficulties setting boundaries, as their basic nature is to please people and make everything pleasant for them. To say no to what people want is the toughest decision for them.

Phosphorus children are prone to fears - namely of the dark (Little Red Riding Hood speaks of the dark when she springs out of the Wolf's tummy), of being alone, of being abandoned, thunder and lightening, and general anxieties.

Finally, this type is summed up by Whitmont (in *'Psyche and Substance'*): "A sociable, sympathetic, pleasant person of rather sanguine temperament, very adaptable, enthusiastic but unreliable, with but little perseverance and strength of character, drifting with the current... given to day-dreaming and romance, sensitive and easily influenced." I think this also sums up our heroine rather well.

Red Riding Hood gets a new birth when she springs out of the tummy of the Wolf; she has learned how to master her weaknesses. When the Wolf swallowed her she was innocent, naive and impressionable .She being tempted by the Wolf indicates to me 'victory' of her vulnerability.

By suggesting *Phosphorus* as a remedy for Little Red Riding Hood or to any other children having archetypes similar to Little Red Riding Hood, we can help our patients 'change' so that they can live their life smoothly in a cohesive direction.

Cases for The Little Red Riding Hood

Case 1

This is the case of an 8 year old child with severe atopic eczema. The child was suffering from eczema for many years and was under various treatments, namely – allopathic, homoeopathic and ayurvedic but there was no improvement subsequently. The child came to me with these suppressed eruptions.

When I started talking with the child, she hardly answered and I immediately suspected that there was some suppression or damage to the child's emotions. I explained this to the mother who accompanied the child during the interview and I asked her to explain to me her life situation ever since she was pregnant, till today.

She informed me that she herself is a chartered accountant, married to a businessman; she was born and brought up in a very healthy atmosphere where a lot of freedom and respect was given to her as a girl, but when she got married there was a lot of stress in her life as her husband was suffering from 'mother fixation.' He would only listen to his mother and never supported his wife, thus leading to a lot of conflicts, clashes of ego, quarrels and humiliation during pregnancy. There were instances where she wanted to curse God for making her pregnant and getting her married in this family. However, she didn't lose hope; she thought, may be after the birth of the child everything would change.

When the child was born, the story continued; again there was not enough support. As she was a working woman, she would come home very tired and would have to take care of the domestic responsibilities as well as of the child.

At a very early age, the child was sent to a care taker or a baby sitter and this is exactly the time frame when the atopic eczema started. There were no particular modalities but the eruptions used to be red, angry and fiery with a lot of scratching which would be worse in the heat and warmth of the bed. The child was found to be allergic to many nutritious food items like wheat, milk, butter and cheese. The child was on lactose free diet (with no milk and diary products) for a long time but there was no improvements with this change also.

The child as she grew, was extremely insecure because the child had witnessed many quarrels, many acts of violence between the parents and that was the main reason why the child spoke very little, especially in the presence of strangers. However, on the other side, what I found out from the mother was that the child was extremely talented, had a good knack of drawing and took a lot of interest in music and dancing. Also, she knew how to play the piano at such a tender age.

When she was not in a bad mood, she was extremely cheerful but she lacked confidence. She was also very meticulous and particular and took good care of her things. Any quarrel or unpleasantness in the family would immediately affect her eczema.

She had a fear of darkness, of the night time, of animals especially cats, of ghosts, of spiders and of loud noises. She slept on her abdomen. She had perspiration, especially on her chest and neck. She could not digest fats and eggs but she loved cheese and onions. She was extremely fascinated with Little Red Riding Hood's story. She identifies herself many times with Red Riding Hood, trying to wear those kinds of clothes, and is strongly attracted to the colour, red. She also liked going to the garden and playing with flowers, exactly like Red Riding Hood. When repeatedly shown the fairy tale cards she always pointed out towards Red Riding Hood.

When we discussed the story further, the child said, "The people who harm my mother are the wolf." But the most important thing that I saw in the case were her fears and anxieties along with the damage to her psychology after witnessing such type of violence.

Thus, I selected *Carcinosinum* 30C; later on, I increased the strength to LM1, LM6 and LM8. Within a span of six months I could completely cure the eczema. Not only that, her fear factors and anxieties were much reduced. She accepted and became more mature about the situation saying that this particular family situation may not change but she has to become stronger. During the homoeopathic treatment, on various occasions she told her mother not to worry and that she was there to protect her.

Case 2

The second case is of a boy with cervical lymphadenopathy and recurrent tonsillitis with enlarged adenoids. The child was 9 years old, tall, slender but very weak and delicate. He was so thin that we could easily count the ribs on his chest. The mother said that in the last few years his growth has been quite rapid.

His main complaint was obstruction of the nose at night; headache was worse in open air, on exertion, when he was sad and due to any excitement. He has a running nose, his nostrils were dilated, and the discharge from the nose was greenish and thick. The nose was obstructed more at night. His facial expressions to me looked quite sickly. He was timid and resolute. He also suffered from dandruff. There was a history of bronchitis where the cold from the nose descended into the chest.

When he started learning to speak, he was tottering. He craves spicy and acidic things. Frequently he gets a burning sensation in his rectum, before and during passing stool. He was quite sleepy during the day, even though he sleeps well at night. His palms were sweaty.

When I inquired about his family situation, I discovered that his father was an alcoholic and a gambler. During the time of pregnancy, his mother was extremely insecure regarding their financial stability because the husband was a gambler and he used to drink beyond limits, would come home and start quarrelling. Hence, there was an element of fright and unhappiness, and the mother suffered from silent grief. She could not discuss this with anybody. After the birth of the child, the situation remained the same for a long time. However, since the past few years, her husband has been making sincere attempts to withdraw himself from alcohol and the family condition was slowly getting normal. Now, the child's ill-health regarding the adenoids that obstruct the breathing, the cervical lymphadenopathy and the child not gaining weight are of a big concern.

The child had been advised tonsillectomy and adenoidectomy. Also, the child has been advised a CT scan of the chest by the pediatrician to rule out any pathology.

When I started the toy therapy, I found that the child was selecting only those toys which have power and strength, as for example, the child took Superman and he said to me - I want to become like Superman so that I can destroy all the bad people in the world. I asked him, who the bad people are, and he answered, "Bad people are those who get angry." I then asked, "Who gets angry?" He answered, "Father and father's family get angry with me and my mother."

He narrated some incidences in the family to me, where there was an episode of anger from the father towards the mother. When I did the fairy tale test, he was persistent on the card of Red Riding Hood because he wanted to run away from home several times, go to the forest like Red Riding Hood and meet his grandmother. I asked him "Where is your grandmother?" He said, "My grandmother lives in a village." I asked him why he wanted to go to his grandmother to which he said, "Whenever I am not happy, whenever my father is angry with my mother or me, I like to run away to my grandmother the way Red Riding Hood went to her grandmother."

I asked him further questions regarding why he was attracted towards Red Riding Hood and he said, "Red Riding Hood is very beautiful, very loving and caring. Even I would like to take good care of my mother and my grandmother." This indicated the affectionate and the sympathetic nature of the child.

With this understanding, I prescribed *Phosphorus* 30C, 200C and later 10M potency where there was a complete resolution of adenoids, tonsils and cervical lymph nodes within a span of five months.

CHAPTER 19

The Little Mermaid

This is a tragic story written by Hans Christian Anderson of Denmark somewhere during the period 1840-1842. There are many different versions of the story including the one by Walt Disney, mainly because many story writers felt that children would not like a sad and depressing ending and hence the need to make the ending more happier, but I have tried to stick to the most original one while describing the story.

Once upon a time, in a splendid palace on the bed of the bluest ocean, lived the Sea King, a wise old triton with a long flowing white beard. He lived in a magnificent palace, built of gaily coloured corals and seashells, together with his five daughters, very beautiful mermaids.

Sirenetta, the youngest and loveliest of them all, also had a beautiful voice, and when she sang, the fishes flocked from all over the sea to listen to her. The shells gaped wide, showing their pearls and even the jellyfish stopped to listen. The young Mermaid often sang, and each time, she would gaze upwards, seeking the faint sunlight that scarcely managed to filter down into the depths.

"Oh, how I'd love to go up there and at last see the sky, which everyone says is so pretty, and hear the voices of humans and smell the scent of the flowers!"

"You're still too young!" said her mother. "In a year or two, when you're fifteen, the King will let you go up there, like your sisters!" Sirenetta spent her time wishing for the world of humans, she listened to her sisters' stories, and every

time they returned from the surface, she would ask them
questions, to satisfy her curiosity.

And as she waited for the day when she too would be
allowed to reach the surface of the sea and meet the unknown
world, Sirenetta spent her time in her wonderful sea garden.
The seahorses kept her company, and sometimes a dolphin would come by and
play. Only the unfriendly starfish never replied when she called. At last, her long
desired birthday came. The night before, Sirenetta could not sleep a wink. In the
morning, her father called her and, stroking her long golden hair, slipped a lovely
carved flower into her locks.

There, now you can go to the surface. You'll breathe air and see the sky. But remember! It's not our world! We can only watch it and admire! We're children of the sea and have no soul, as men do. Be careful and keep away from them; they can only bring bad luck!" In a second, Sirenetta had kissed her father and was darting smoothly towards the surface of the sea. She swam so fast with flicks of her slender tail that even the fish could not keep up with her.

Suddenly she popped out of the water. How wonderful! For the first time, she saw the great blue sky, in which as dusk began to fall, the first stars were peeping out and twinkling. The sun, already over the horizon, trailed a golden reflection that gently faded on the heaving waves. High overhead, a flock of gulls spotted the Little Mermaid and greeted her arrival with shrieks of pleasure.

"It's so lovely!" she exclaimed happily. But another nice surprise was in store for her – a ship was slowly sailing towards the rock on which Sirenetta was sitting. The sailors dropped anchor and the ship swayed gently in the calm sea. Sirenetta watched the men go about their work aboard, lighting the lanterns for the night. She could clearly hear their voices.

"I'd love to speak to them!" she said to herself. But then she gazed sadly at her long flexible tail, her equivalent of legs, and said to herself, — "I can never be like them!" Aboard ship, a strange excitement seemed to seize the crew, and a little later, the sky became a spray of many coloured lights and the crackle of fireworks filled the sky.

"Long live the captain! Hurray for his twentieth birthday. Hurray! Hurray! Many happy returns!" Astonished at all this, the Little Mermaid caught sight of the young man in whose honour the display was being held. Tall and dignified, he was smiling happily, and Sirenetta could not take her eyes from him. She followed his every movement, fascinated by all that was happening. The party went on, but the sea grew more agitated. Sirenetta anxiously realized that the men were now in danger — an icy wind was sweeping the waves, the ink black sky was torn by flashes of lightening and then a terrible storm broke suddenly over the helpless ship. In vain, Sirenetta screamed, "Look out! Beware of the sea . . ." But the howling wind carried her words away, and the rising waves swept over the ship. Amidst the sailors' shouts, the masts and sails toppled onto the deck, and with a sinister splintering sound, the ship sank.

By the light of one of the oil lamps the young captain fall into the water, and she swam to his rescue. But she could not find him in the high waves. Tired, she was about to give up her search, when suddenly there he was, on the crest of a nearby wave. In an instant, he was swept straight into the Mermaid's arms.

The young man was unconscious and the Mermaid held his head above water in the stormy sea, in an effort to save his life. She clung to him for hours trying to fight the tiredness that was overtaking her.

Then, as suddenly as it had sprung up, the storm died away. In a grey dawn over a still angry sea, Sirenetta realized thankfully that land lay ahead. Aided by the motion of the waves, she pushed the Captain's body onto the shore, beyond

the water's edge. Unable herself to walk, the Mermaid sat wringing her hands, her tail lapped by the rippling water, trying to warm the young Captain with her own body. Then the sound of approaching voices startled Sirenetta and she slipped back into deeper water.

"Come quickly! Quickly!" came a woman's voice in alarm. "There's a man here! Look, I think he's unconscious!" The Captain was now in good hands.

"Let's take him up to the castle!"

"No, no! Better get help . . ." And the first thing the young man saw when he opened his eyes again was the beautiful face of the youngest of a group of three ladies.

"Thank you! Thank you . . . for saving my life . . ." he murmured to the lovely unknown lady.

From the sea, Sirenetta watched the man she had snatched from the waves turn towards the castle, without knowing that a mermaid had saved his life. Slowly swimming out to sea, Sirenetta felt that there on the beach she had left behind something she could never bring herself to forget. How wonderful those tremendous hours in the storm had been, as she had battled with the elements. And as she swam down towards her father's palace, her sisters came to meet her, anxious to know what had kept her so long on the surface. Sirenetta started to tell her story, but suddenly a lump came to her throat and, bursting into tears, she fled to her room. She stayed there for days, refusing to see anyone or to touch any food. She knew that her love for the young Captain was without hope, for she was a mermaid and could never marry a human.

Only the Witch of the Deeps could help her. But what price would she have to pay? Sirenetta decided to ask the Witch. ". . . so you want to get rid of your fishy tail, do you? I expect you'd like to have a pair of woman's legs, isn't that so?" said the nasty Witch scornfully, from her cave guarded by a giant squid.

"Be warned!" she went on, "You will suffer horribly, as though a sword were cutting you apart. And every time you place your feet on the earth, you will feel dreadful pain!"

"It doesn't matter!" whispered Sirenetta, with tears in her eyes. "As long as I can go back to him!"

"And that's not all!" exclaimed the Witch. "In exchange for my spell, you must give me your lovely voice. You'll never be able to utter a word again! And don't forget! If the man you love marries someone else, you will not be able to turn into a mermaid again. You will just dissolve in water like the foam on the wave!"

"All right!" said Sirenetta, eagerly taking the little jar holding the magic potion. The Witch had told Sirenetta that the young Captain was actually a prince, and the Mermaid left the water at a spot not far from the castle. She pulled herself onto the beach, and then drank the magic potion. An agonizing pain made her faint, and when she came to her senses, she could mistily see the face she loved, smiling down at her.

The Witch's magic had worked the spell, for the Prince had felt a strange desire to go down to the beach, just as Sirenetta was arriving. There he had stumbled on her, and recalling how he too had once been washed up on the shore, gently laid his cloak over the still body, cast up by the waves.

"Don't be frightened! he said quickly. "You're quite safe! Where have you come from?" But Sirenetta was now dumb and could not reply, so the young man softly stroked her wet cheek.

"I'll take you to the castle and look after you," he said. In the days that followed, the Mermaid started a new life. She wore splendid dresses and often went out on horseback with the Prince. One evening, she was invited to a great ball at Court. However, as the Witch had foretold, every movement and each step she took was torture. Sirenetta bravely put up with her suffering, glad to be allowed to stay near her beloved prince. And though she could not speak to him, he was fond of her and showered kindness on her, to her great joy. However, the young man's heart really belonged to the unknown lady he had seen as he lay on the shore, though he had never met her since, for she had returned at once to her own land.

Even when he was in the company of Sirenetta, fond of her as he was, the unknown lady was always in her thoughts. And the Little Mermaid, guessing instinctively that she was not his true love, suffered even more.

She often crept out of the castle at night, to weep by the seashore. Once she thought she could spy her sister's rise from the water and wave at her, but this made her feel sadder than ever.

Fate, however, had another surprise in store. From the Castle ramparts one day, a huge ship was sighted sailing into the harbour. Together with Sirenetta, the Prince went down to meet it. And who stepped from the vessel, but the unknown lady who had been for long in the Prince's heart. When he saw her, he rushed to greet her. Sirenetta felt herself turn to stone and a painful feeling pierced her heart, she was about to lose the prince forever. The unknown lady too had never forgotten the young man she had found on the beach and soon after, he asked her to marry him. Since she too was in love, she happily said "Yes."

A few days after the wedding, the happy couple was invited for a voyage on the huge ship, which was still in the harbour. Sirenetta too went on board, and the ship set sail. Night fell, and sick at heart over the loss of the Prince, Sirenetta went on deck. She remembered the Witch's prophecy, and was now ready to give up her life and dissolve in the sea. Suddenly she heard a cry from the water and dimly saw her sisters in the darkness. "Sirenetta! Sirenetta! It's us, your sisters! We've heard all about what happened! Look! Do you see this knife? It's magic! The Witch gave it to us in exchange for our hair. Take it! Kill the Prince before dawn, and you will become a mermaid again and forget all your troubles!"

As though in a trance, Sirenetta clasped the   knife and entered the cabin where the Prince and his bride lay asleep. But as she gazed at the young man's sleeping face, she simply blew him a furtive kiss, before running back on deck. When dawn broke, she threw the knife into the sea. Then she shot a parting glance at the world she was leaving behind, and dived into the waves, ready to turn into the foam of the sea from whence she had come, and vanish.

As the sun rose over the horizon, it cast a long golden ray of light across the sea, and in the chilly water, Sirenetta turned towards it for the last time. Suddenly, as though by magic, a mysterious force drew her out of the water, and she felt herself lifted high into the sky. The clouds were tinged with pink, the sea rippled in the early morning breeze, and the Little Mermaid heard a whisper through the tinkling of bells: "Sirenetta, Sirenetta! Come with us".

"Who are you?" asked the Mermaid, surprised to find she had recovered the use of her voice. "Where am I?"

"You're with us in the sky. We're the fairies of the air! We have no soul as men do, but our task is to help them. We take amongst us only those who have shown kindness to men!"

Greatly touched, Sirenetta looked down over the sea towards the Prince's ship, and felt tears spring to her eyes. The fairies of the air whispered to her: "Look! The earth's flowers are waiting for our tears to turn into the morning dew! Come along with us ..."

Homoeopathic Interpretation

Now let us understand the rubrics of Little Mermaid:

MIND - AILMENTS FROM - abused; after being
MIND - AILMENTS FROM - love; disappointed
MIND - AILMENTS FROM - love; disappointed - grief, with silent
MIND - AILMENTS FROM - love; disappointed - sadness, with
MIND - DISCONTENTED
MIND - FATALISTIC
MIND - GRIEF - silent - love; from disappointed
MIND - HELPLESSNESS; feeling of
MIND - IMPULSIVE
MIND - INDIFFERENCE - future, to
MIND - INDIFFERENCE - stoical to what happens
MIND - LOVE - romantic love; desire for
MIND - MARTYR
MIND-SINGING

| MIND - SACRIFICING |
| MIND - SENTIMENTAL |
| MIND - SYMPATHETIC |

The Mermaid's rubrics are many but I have managed to select the most important ones, now if I analyze *The Little Mermaid,* she is:

- Curious to see the world outside

- Discontented and unsatisfied with her present circumstances

- Romantic and is a true lover who can do anything for her beau

- Impulsive and extemporaneous

- Reckless and foolhardy

- Brave and valiant

- Sacrifices herself for love in a way that smacks of martyrdom

- Hopelessness, leading to suicide, which she does in a very self-effacing and accepting manner

- She is a character with whom we feel sympathy, frustration, anger and, finally, despair — most of the time we would probably want to just shake her! There is something of the 'battered wife' about her those that say they are incapable of leaving their violent marriages 'because I love him.'

The remedies which match the archetype of the Little Mermaid are *Pulsatilla pratensis, Carcinosinum, Ignatia amara, Phosphorus* and possibly *Natrium muriaticum.*

To begin with, let me start with *Ignatia amara* who is quite idealistic in her thinking process. The story is loaded with powerful love of the Little Mermaid for the Captain with a feeling of letting go or sacrificing to win this love which is later followed by silent grief. *Ignatia amara* is represented in the repertory for ailments from disappointment in love, disappointment with silent grief, disappointment in love with sadness. Also, *Ignatia amara* does not have any shame or bitterness with disappointment which it's counterpart *Natrium muriaticum* is associated with. On the contrary, they accept with stoicism, the fate they have chosen. This is the main reason why I would think of *Ignatia amara*. The whole story of the Little Mermaid is full of sacrifices and ultimately she achieves nothing.

Pulsatilla pratensis is another remedy in queue; the Mermaid is very loving, affectionate, mild like any other heroine of the fairy tale. What the character lacks is the selfishness or timidity which is typically seen in this remedy. One more thing that goes against *Pulsatilla pratensis* is the self-sacrificing and non-demanding nature of the Little Mermaid.

Carcinosinum, is the best match for the character of Little Mermaid. The theme of self-sacrifice for the sake of love, losing her own identity by losing her tail, undergoing severe pain every time she walked with human legs and finally the way she ends her life and saves the life of her lover by not murdering him with the knife which her sister gives her, typifies *Carcinosinum.*

Carcinosinum, I have seen in my practice can go to any extent to give others the necessities to fulfil their dream. Unfortunately, the story takes a sad turn by forcing the Little Mermaid to commit suicide which falls flat on the face of the romance she yearned for. She pays a very high price for being so deeply in love with the Captain.

CHAPTER 20

Hero in Fairy Tales

Who is a hero? Our Old Testament had many heroes like - Abraham, Joseph, Moses, Ruth, David, etc. According to Greek mythology and folklore, a hero was originally a demigod, the offspring of a mortal and a deity, their cult being one of the most distinctive features of ancient Greek religion. Later, hero (male) and heroine (female) came to refer to characters (fictional or historical) that, in the face of danger and adversity, or from a position of weakness, display courage and the will for self-sacrifice — that is, heroism — for some greater good, originally of martial courage or excellence but extended to more general moral excellence.

Stories of heroism may serve as moral examples. In classical antiquity, hero cult's veneration of deified heroes such as Heracles, Perseus and Achilles played an important role in ancient Greek religion. Politicians, ancient and modern, have employed hero worship for their own apotheosis (that is, cult of personality).

The traditional quest for hero is assumed to be a male who is separated from his known world, is initiated into a new consciousness, and then returns to his community. (According to Campbell, in traditional mythologies, women usually represent creation and ultimate wisdom, and therefore don't need to make a journey.)

In chapter 15 of 'Poetics', Aristotle describes the tragic hero as a protagonist who is otherwise perfect except for a tragic or fatal flaw that eventually leads to his demise. In fact, an Aristotelian tragic hero must have four characteristics:

goodness, superiority, a tragic flaw and a realization of both - his flaw and his inevitable demise.

In the course of his journey, the hero will encounter other archetypal characters that typically either aid or hinder the hero in his or her quest. Among the most prominent of these is the Sage (a helper), the Trickster (sometimes helpful, sometimes not), and the Shadow (often the villain).

A hero has to win, and the villain has to lose, so the first thing these heroes and heroines do is face challenges. They face up to some hideous beast as Little Red Riding Hood faced the wicked wolf or Beauty did in

'Beauty and the Beast.' Thereafter they recover something that is strongly guarded as Jack does in 'Jack and the Beanstalk;' or they survive an ordeal like Red Riding Hood or Hansel and Gretel.

Another hero that I know is simple, naive, innocent, child-like, and artless; they are usually youngest of the three to four brothers. 'Puss in Boots,' 'Jack and the Beanstalk' are examples of this genre.

In homoeopathic language, if I have to interpret a hero, the following rubrics will tell us all about the attributes of the dashing heroes of fairy tale:

MIND - ACHIEVE things, desire to
MIND - ADVENTUROUS
MIND - AMBITION - increased
MIND - COURAGEOUS
MIND - DEEDS - great deeds; sensation as if he could do
MIND - DELUSIONS - better than others; he is
MIND - DELUSIONS - emperor - is an
MIND - DELUSIONS - great person; is a
MIND - DELUSIONS - power - all-powerful; she is
MIND - DELUSIONS - prince; he is a
MIND - DELUSIONS - strong; he is
MIND - DELUSIONS - superhuman; is
MIND - FEARLESS
MIND - FIGHT, wants to
MIND - INJUSTICE, cannot support
MIND - TRAVELLING - desire for

The most important remedy I think that has the maximum attributes is *Veratrum album*. They are ambitious in achieving their goal; goal oriented, they can fight for injustice and they possess a very charming and attractive personality. To attract the heroine, they can be affectionate in words and gestures and also when given a chance, they can flatter and embrace people around. I have seen

Veratrum album heroes to be very hardworking and reaching their goal with astounding persistency.

Another remedy that I would like to discuss is *Tuberculinum bovinum* kent. *Tuberculinum* individuals have the hunger of experiencing things in an adventurous way. They need action and motion; steady routine life bores them; their life has to be packed with excitement.

More than any other type, they are subject to that awful feeling that they are missing out, whenever the hectic pace of their life slows down, and they are left without stimulation. The *Tuberculinum* individual has inherited from his consumptive ancestors a restless hunger to experience more of life before it ends. Many *Tuberculinums* find an outlet for their restlessness through an aggressive pursuit of sports. *Tuberculinum's* restlessness is not aimless. It is accompanied by a drive for stimulation, which prompts *Tuberculinum* individuals to aggressively enter into new experiences. Fights, wants to be in, and sensitive to any kind of injustice are two very important qualities of heroes which are present in *Tuberculinum bovinum kent*.

Some small remedies like *Cannabis indica*, characterised by a delusion that he is Superman, that he is powerful, or is an emperor, etc., can also be considered for discussion. The only drawback is that *Cannabis indica* is full of euphoric ecstasy with deep depression. Also, all perceptions, sensations and emotions are exaggerated to the utmost degree.

Cocainum hydrochloricum is another small remedy that I feel can cover some qualities of heroes for example, increased ambition; desire to do great deeds by undertaking vast feats of strength and fearlessness. The only contradictory thing in it's image is that *Cocainum hydrochloricum* is very loquacious with frightful persecutory hallucinations, and their moral sense is quite blunted.

There is another type of hero we see in homoeopathy, who are intelligent but not smart , brave and dashing but still in their own way are heroes because ultimately they win and conquer; yes I am talking about *Baryta carbonica*.

Bailey says of *Baryta carbonica*: "Most *Baryta carbonica*'s receive more than their fair share of taunts and ridicule as children (as do the fairy tale '*Simpletons*'), and this leaves them with a constant fear of being laughed at (Kent: Imagine being abused), just as with the description of these types above."

Baryta carbonica's are often child-like in their trust and openness, just as Jack ('*Jack and the Beanstalk*') is when he sets out to sell the one family asset, their cow, and receives five beans in exchange. Luckily for him, his naivety is rewarded, as the beans are magical. Jack is described in the story as brainless, lethargic, sluggish and laggard at understanding. He is always being punished by his baffled mother. The youngest son of the miller in the fairy tale '*Puss in the Boots*' is akin. On his father's death, he receives only a cat. He is laughed at and disgraced as he has been all his life and he seems to accept this only, the cat is magical of course, and his luck is overturned. We instinctively understand that without this magical helper he is useless and rather dim-witted.

This youngest son is, I think, an excellent imitation of the *Baryta carbonica* type, whose jejune singleness wins the admiration of the King, the love of the Princess and an enormous castle, all without him having any idea how he did it.

In the fairy tale *'The Three Feathers'* the King sends his three sons on a quest to find the most beautiful carpet, thus deciding which one will inherit his kingdom. He initiates this by blowing three feathers into the air, and each brother must follow his feather wherever it may go. From the start we know that the youngest son will confound expectations by accomplishing what his brothers cannot. His feather falls to the ground and he has to go into the ground, where a magical Toad helps him.

Because of his simplicity, the youngest son has not yet learned what makes sense and what doesn't, so he responds with all the openness of a child. Vermeulen says of *Baryta carbonica* that he is frozen in a state of child-like emotional arrest. He cannot handle complexities, and this is tacitly understood in the fairy tale. The magical helper in all these types of stories makes his decisions for him, and gives him a set of instructions to follow.

Baryta carbonica too, has lack of self-confidence and strong irresolution; it often responds better to rules where there is no decision to make (Hahnemann describes it as 'Long wavering between opposing resolutions').

Interestingly, it is *Baryta carbonica* (simpleton) who usually wins the day, in spite of not being ambitious and lacking any kind of drive. The magical helpers they are given (the Cat, the Toad and so on) provide the knowledge for them to do so.

Baryta carbonica is often seen hiding behind someone more powerful (their mother usually), or someone they trust.

Pulsatilla pratensis is often compared to *Baryta carbonica*, and I think it is no accident that other heroes and heroines, who may not be as 'simple' and slow as *Baryta carbonica*, match this remedy; such as the Queen in Rumpelstiltskin.

CHAPTER 21

Villains in Fairy Tales

airy tales are full of blackguards, malefactors, miscreants, wretches and devils. They form the essential element without whom there would be no story, nothing against which to fight or make a moral point. They provide the contrast to the worthy heroes and heroines and, of course, most of the action. They are often the most colourful characters — vividly remaining in the mind after the story has been read.

There are two types of villains in fairy tales:

1. A family member — such as a bad uncle, father or wicked stepmother

2. A combatant — somebody the hero or heroine meets and fights, such as a giant, a wicked witch, a strange creature like Rumpelstiltskin, a horrible ogre, or a wild animal like a wolf or a bear except the Beast in Beauty and the Beast that looks like a villain but is not, and the frog of the Frog Prince.

What does a villain do?

- He either causes harm to the hero or heroine and their family

- He competes with the hero or fights with him

- He pursues the hero after he has succeeded in winning the fight or obtaining something from the villain

None of these acts must necessarily occur in a fairy tale, but when they do, the character that performed them was the villain. The villain therefore could

appear twice: once in the opening of the story, and a second time as the person sought out by the hero.

Some examples from the fairy tale book are as follows:

Cinderella's Stepmother made her work hard and kept her from parties and fun, but she got tons of help from a Fairy Godmother, the glass slipper fitted her and she lived happily ever after.

Snow White's Stepmom made her eat a poisoned apple because she was jealous...but she wakes up to the kiss of a Prince.

Rumpelstiltskin insisted on making the Queen give up her first born child.... but it didn't work, she guessed his name and he had to go away.

The worst villain is the witch in Hansel and Gretel. Imagine, luring children with a candy house and then putting them in the oven! The parents in that story weren't exactly mom and dad representation, sending the kids out into the forest to fend for them and hopefully disappear, but a representation of dangers of life outside a safe home.

Let's look on the subject of collective unconscious. As I understand it is a pond of memories, ideas, and modes of thought that comes from the experiences of life. It coexists with the personal unconscious, which contains the material of individual experience, and may be regarded as an immense depository of ancestral sagacity.

The images of the villains which we read in the fairy tales have a strong influence on our collective unconsciousness and embody powerful forces in the psyche. Carl Jung made it very clear, it is not the images themselves that we inherit, but the tendency to create and use them. Dr Edmond Whitmont puts it as, "Imaginal or symbolic thinking, that is imaging, the experiencing of form-patterns or configurationally wholes, is thus an inner expression of our oneness with outer reality." He equates the imaging we do in fairy tales (as well as in myths, dreams and fantasy) to the imaging or personification of remedies. We give each remedy a personality 'type.' "Each with his typical physical traits and emotional personality as well as particular pathology propensities." Thus, we may image a substance as if it had an external personality.

The child's mind is full of chaos that is, loaded with contradictory feelings as compared to adults who have learned to rationalize these feelings; the child is submerged by all the uncertainties within himself. He experiences the infatuation, passion, fondness, detestation, terror, panic, acrimony and so on within himself. He cannot engineer his feelings, at one and the same time, both good, as in obedient, and bad, as in rebellious. They either love or hate, and nothing is in shades of grey. This is how the child views the fairy tale world; it's figures are either all open handed, full of good will, or of devouring beasts. Every figure is one-dimensional and it is by portraying it this way that the tale enables the child to sort out his own complex and ambivalent feelings. In other words, he learns to sort some order out of the chaos.

Let us examine different archetypes of villains in fairy tales who come to us in different shades of mother, stepmother, or witch. Mother is the most fundamental attachment of the child; hence fear of being abandoned by her is of gigantic importance in child psychology.

In *'Hansel and Gretel,'* there is an actual Stepmother who is pitiless enough to throw them out into the forest. This is a contrary representation of the maternal symbol.

Cinderella and Snow White both have wicked Stepmothers. Rapunzel, on the other hand, has a real mother who gives her up at birth as promised and she is looked after by a witch who looks after her like a mother but overly so. She is locked up in a tall tower and allowed to see no one representing selfish, over-protective mothering.

There was an era from 1700-1875 in the history that was called as 'Witch Sporting.' It was also during this same period that many fairy tales were written and read by people all over the Europe. Thus, many people started strongly believing in Witches and it didn't take much to be suspected of being a Witch either.

Jung says in his popular book, *'Man and His Symbols'* that in the middle ages, the wild world of the unconscious was recognized more clearly than before. The knightly cult of the lady truly differentiated the feminine side of man's nature: a personification of the anima. Later this became fused with the figure of the Virgin. When the anima, as Virgin, was conceived as being all positive, her negative aspects then found expression in the belief in witches.

Another, more subtle, manifestation of a negative anima appears in some fairy tales in the form of a princess who asks her suitors to answer a series of riddles, or perhaps to hide themselves under her nose. If they cannot give the answers, or if she can find them, they must die. And she usually wins.

Homoeopathic remedies which I think suit the archetypal of the characters mentioned above are: *Sepia officinalis* for those Mothers or Stepmothers who have become *'driven to the point of exhaustion, cut off from and repressing her feminine balance and intuition.'* (Whitmont). These types are essentially animus-ridden often domineering, irritable and lacking in emotional responsiveness (cold shoulder type). They show an aversion or indifference to family, husband and children (all loved ones), with a compulsive need to withdraw when under emotional strain. The Stepmother in *'Hansel and Gretel'* and the Mother in *'Rapunzel'* represent *Sepia officinalis* very beautifully.

The next in the list for Stepmothers of fairy tales is *Anacardium orientale,* *Hyoscyamus niger* and *Lachesis mutus*. These typify the jealousy felt by an older woman for a young and beautiful one, even if that happens to be her own daughter.

The Queen in *'Snow White and the Seven Drawfs'* matches *Hyoscyamus niger,* since her jealousy leads her to plot a murder; whereas the Stepmother in *'Cinderella'* with her ugly sisters, and the Wicked Fairy in *'Sleeping Beauty'*, all belong to the family of *Lachesis mutus*. It is typical of *Lachesis mutus* for the woman, in Whitmont's words, to "sever her psychologically from all the life impulses.' They repress and cut off vital forces as a price to be paid for personal and personality development.

Anacardium orientale fits quite well the personality of the Witch in the fairy tale *'Hansel and Gretel.'* She is sinister and heinous in her acts. *Anacardium orientale* is known for it's atrocious deeds. *Anacardium orientale* as a drug picture is full of abuse, violent anger, brutality, cruelty and depravity. Devil and angel sitting on the shoulder of the same person giving opposite commands has it's undercurrent in the religious influence of the Catholic Church, which was strong enough to influence a common man in the Victorian era.

The Witch or Devil in fairy tales represents part of our 'shadow' (Jung's term for the sin or guilt inherent in all of us). Shadow is the store house of our dark side which we want to hide from the world. By comparing the Witch in the fairy tale with his or her shadow, the child unconditionally makes his conscious as the hero that differentiates between villain and hero (our conscious). In all fairy tales in the end the hero wins and the villain or the evil looses thereby producing victory of divine or morals laws. This makes the reader of the fairy tale feel victorious as the shadow has lost and the conscious has won.

The commonly agreed attitude to good and evil in fairy tales is largely determined by Christianity as these tales were written in those times and in that society where Christianity had much influence. Even those who say they are atheists and have no sense of religion are subject to similar attitude; as human culture is so much influenced by religion from the very start. These tales can be seen really, as a way of simplifying complex metaphysical problems, as in the story of the Garden of Eden.

Eden represents paradise and wholeness, whereas polarity is represented by the two trees of good and evil. In original Hebrew, the world which translates as rib (from which Eve is made) is related to the word 'tsel' or shadow. Adam and Eve live in the wholeness of paradise, until along comes the serpent who promises Eve that eating from the Tree of Knowledge will enable them both to distinguish between good and evil. This knowledge shatters their sense of completeness and contentment: they are now forever trying to hide and feel divided. It is a truth that good and evil resides in all of us, and the one depends on the other. Temptation is also a common theme in fairy tales (echoing this original story of temptation): for often than not the hero or heroine will succumb, only to have to fight their way back to the moral high ground, and be all the better for it.

Children are not capable of self-knowledge and enlightenment (which is a journey that happens with maturity). So the fairy stories with their monsters, giants, heroes and magic can act out their frightening shadow side for them — thus bringing consciousness to it, a welcoming light, a lessening of the fear that it has such a grip on them, and ultimately, lessen the shadow.

In homoeopathic terms, 'evil in the medical context is sickness' (according to Ortega in his *Notes on the Miasms*). This makes sense: if evil lies within and is something with which we are all familiar, it represents a disruption, a disorder, a disease in our being.

We have to make the symptom (or signal) unnecessary, by letting into our consciousness whatever we are lacking; healing involves an expansion of our consciousness. Given that the symptom arose in the first place because part of our shadow found it's way into the body, and manifested itself there, healing is simply the same process in reverse. The issue behind the symptom is made conscious and so is released from existing physically.

Kent says in homoeopathy we talk of sick individuals. Here along with the sick body, he refers to sick will and intellect of the person that needs to be treated, "With the will and understanding in order, we have a healthy man."

Anacardium orientale is a perfect example of lack of balance between good and evil forces. In *Anacardium orientale* there are two wills antagonising each other.

The rubric which describes this is:

MIND - DELUSIONS - devil - speaking in one ear, prompting to murder - angel in the other ear, prompting to acts of benevolence; and an
MIND - WILL - two wills; sensation as if he had
MIND - WILL - two wills; sensation as if he had - commanding what the other forbids; one

It is a useful remedy in persons whose shadow side begins to emerge, that is, where the parts of ourselves which we, or others, have labelled 'bad' and suppressed begin to demand attention.

Violence in *Anacardium orientale* is sometimes seen as the only way to control an overwhelming lack of confidence, from which they typically suffer.

Remedies, apart from *Anacardium orientale*, that might represent this shadow side of the psyche must emphasise negative traits, such as lack of control, maliciousness, spite, violent impulses and quick anger. One such remedy is *Hyoscyamus niger,* which I discussed with relation to Snow White, and another is *Veratrum album*. This is a particularly unpleasant remedy; people needing this are often pessimistic moaners who almost seem to take pride in their unpleasantness. There is a feeling with *Veratrum album* that they can't be trusted and they do lie compulsively. They will always think of something bad to say of someone else and lack empathy for others. They tend to be domineering, irritable, critical people who lack warmth, and hold a grudge for a long time.

The Sea-Witch typifies this personality type, I feel, in that she is desperate to be the Queen of the Ocean (*Veratrum album* has 'delusions of grandeur' and worry about their place in society) and seeks to control the destiny of others.

In the story of the Mermaid, the villain (Witch) takes delight in ruling and ruining the lives of those in the story. In true *Veratrum album* style she is quite cleverly deceitful, drawing the Little Mermaid in under pretence of kindness, only to show her true colours later. The remedy often has a sort of charisma about it, an indefinable something that attracts people.

It is also a remedy which can be coldly malicious — and the Sea-Witch certainly shows no mercy, when the Mermaid finds herself at the end in an impossible situation.

In *Veratrum album*, we frequently see a sort of insanity that can lead to severe violent mania where one can do evil deeds of violence. In this story the Sea-Witch does not use violence to achieve her ends; instead, she cleverly plots and manipulates the situation to her own ends. With *Veratrum album* the end justifies the means: if they have to lie, then they will (and they are liars above all else). The Sea-Witch has no compunction about telling the Little Mermaid that she will achieve the love she yearns for, while at the same time making her mute, and causing her feet to bleed horribly when she moves. It is hardly the best way to go about attracting a Prince!

Stramonium is the next villain worth discussion. What I see here is a volcano of violence accompanied by strong fears that come from the unconscious mind. It is one remedy which is completely out of balance; on one hand you have rage and anger and on the other hand you see severe depression.

In a breakdown, the *Stramonium* state is highly agitated, active, driven and possibly violent, with hallucinations, convulsions and constant uncoordinated movements. The person may be restless and raging, very destructive and violent, wanting to fight, bite, take off or tear up the clothes and smash things. A sufferer is incoherently talkative, compulsively shouting and swearing; they suffer fear too, especially of the dark or shining surfaces, and being attacked by animals.

Destructiveness and violence are characteristic symptoms of this remedy. It is a remedy that has truly lost the struggle for control. Reading a story where a character exhibits these traits can be comforting, if that character is then defeated at the end of the story. Children can understand, without having it spelt out, that the evil within can be defeated.

Stramonium, above all, bears the anxiety about being devoured; when we look in the repertory, the following rubrics come up:

MIND - FEAR - devoured by animals; of being
MIND - DELUSIONS - animals - devoured by
MIND - DELUSIONS - devoured by animals

Dr Dider Grandgeorge mentions in his book *'The Spirit of Homoeopathy'* that from time immemorial, when wild animals learned through their natural instincts the ability to devour a victim with the help of their paws, claws and teeth, in the similar way, the little human baby develops a similar anxiety when it is passing through the 'oral stage' of psycho-sexual development, from the time when the teeth come in; the child can bite, but can also be bitten... and so we have corresponding stories of ogres as in *'Jack and the Beanstalk;'* wolves, in *'Little Red Riding Hood,'* *'The Three Little Pigs;'* etc. Dr Grandgeorge refers to the 'spirit' of this remedy as 'devour or be devoured.'

Children often go through a stage of having night terrors, where they wake up screaming in the middle of the night, pushing away familiar faces like their mother, clearly terrified. *Stramonium* is more often than not successful in dealing with these. It is a remedy that is easily enervated by bright light, running water or social contact, yet on the other hand is afraid of silence and the dark. It is no coincidence that forests and dark forbidding places with wild animals roaming around are so prominently found in fairy tales.

Stramonium is usually thought when a fearful and wild aspect of the person is seen; it is very useful when suddenly one sees sudden emergence of suppressed or repressed shadow that emerges from the unconscious mind, mainly under the influence of severe stress.

In *Stramonium* fear and violence is masked (in *Thuja occidentalis* it is sexual urges and sexual guilt), but when the violence comes on the surface, it comes in it's most severe form mentioned below:

MIND - ABUSIVE
MIND - ANGER - sudden
MIND - ANGER - violent
MIND - ATTACK others, desire to
MIND - BITING - people
MIND - BREAKING things
MIND - CRUELTY
MIND - DESTRUCTIVENESS
MIND - MANIA - rage, with
MIND - RAGE - biting, with
MIND - RAGE - chained, had to be
MIND - RAGE - kill people, tries to
MIND - RAGE - violent

Wild animals do have a close association in fairy tales. The Wolf from 'Little Red Riding Hood' is one such example. The Wolf tries his best to charm the cute and naive Little Red Riding Hood, similar to how a *Stramonium* child in his grace and attraction would play with another child and then suddenly push him down on to the ground. Like *Belladonna*, *Stramonium* can strike with great suddenness. There is a sudden shift in social graces and the child falls into the abyss of hell.

The Wolf, once informed of Little Red Riding Hood's intention, sneaks off to Grandma's cottage, impersonates the little girl's voice to get in, and devours the old lady. This is always fairly shocking to relate at this point — and interestingly this story is notably violent and has been subject to the most politically-correct revisions. The violence, of course, is in-keeping with *Stramonium*. A little while later, Little Red Riding Hood enters the cottage, and there follows one of the most famous interchanges in fairy tale history:

"O Grandmother, what big ears you've got,
The better to hear you with, my dear.
Grandmother, what big eyes you've got,
The better to see you with, my dear.
Grandmother, what big hands you've got,
The better to catch hold of you, my dear.
But, Grandmother, what big teeth you've got,
The better to eat you up with my dear"

Majority of children who listen to this immediately scream or develop severe fear with shock. There may be few kids who after hearing what happened to Little Red Riding Hood start weeping.

The Wolf is shown to be sweetness itself as he answers the questions in Grandmother's bed but his deception makes him all the more frightening, and the suddenness of his attack is another shock. Grimm says simply, "Hardly had the Wolf said this, than he made a spring out of bed and devoured poor Red Riding Hood."

Usually, *Stramonium* children are fascinated by violence. They pick up knives and have fantasies or images of cutting their own or others' flesh (Kent: 'Persistent thoughts of homicide') and they can be seen to follow salacious stories of violence in the media. Look at the rubrics selected from Synthesis Repertory; this will give you an idea about Stramonium and violence:

MIND - AILMENTS FROM - violence
MIND - ANGER - violent
MIND - DELIRIUM - violent
MIND - DELUSIONS - violent
MIND - GESTURES, makes - violent
MIND - IMPULSE; morbid - violence, to do

MIND - INSANITY - violent
MIND - MANIA - violence, with deeds of
MIND - MUTILATING his body
MIND - RAGE - violent
MIND - SPEECH - violent
MIND - WEEPING - violent

In the fairy tale, the Wolf is cut open while he sleeps off his meal of grandmother and Little Red Riding Hood. Grimm dwells on the slashes that are needed to find first the little girl and then the old woman. At the end, the Huntsman skinned the Wolf and all is seen to be resolved. Those who seek to eat others are devoured themselves.

When Little Red Riding Hood springs out of the Wolf's abdomen she says, "I was extremely frightened inside; it was so dark." *Stramonium* has great fears of dark, closed places.

In this story, the Wolf represents symbolically a male rake, and an 'animal' side of the person.

The same can be said, effectively, for the other villains of fairy tales, who come in the form of giants, stepmothers and trolls. They seem to me, to typify the same *Stramonium* characteristics as, the wolf in *'Little Red Riding Hood'* or *'The Three Little Pigs.'*

The rubrics 'brutality', 'cruelty', 'jealousy', 'unfelling' and 'wicked' describes these types of baddies. In our homoeopathic repertories, these qualities are seen in remedies like: *Absinthium, Alcoholus, Anacardium orientale, Curare, Lachesis mutus, Sarracenia purpurea, Stramonium, Tarentula hispanica,* etc.

These types of villains do not operate cunningly with stealth but bellow and bark and crash about; they can also be violent. The rubric 'bellowing' lists *Belladonna, Cantharis vesicatoria,* and *Cuprum metallicum.* The rubric 'violent' gives us totally 134 remedies; the important ones include — *Cicuta virosa, Hepar sulphurus, Hyoscyamus niger.*

Let's discuss *Cicuta virosa* as I have not discussed it so far. They are reserved, introverted individuals who are too distant or close from others and their emotions. They are quite estranged from their family and society in general; any social contact makes them angry, violent and contemptuous.

There is a depreciation and contempt of mankind; "he fled from his fellow-creatures, was in the highest degree disgusted with their follies, and his disposition seemed to change into misanthropy; he withdrew into solitude." – Hahnemann

This makes him very antisocial; on rare occasions, he may indulge in deeds of violence. He also does not trust people easily. This makes him very suspicious – *"Want of trust in people and anthrophoby; he fled from them, remained solitary, and thought seriously about their errors and about himself." –* Hahnemann

He desires absolute solitude. He indulges in his fear of mankind with situations that demand social contact where he may become very angry, abusive or may even land up in a maniacal delirium.

Next remedy on my list is *Hydrophobinum*. This is the remedy that aptly suits the villains of fairy tales, especially the wolf, witches and the demons.

Both domestic and feral dogs are carnivorous members of the *Canidae* family. They have been helpers for humans ever since these canines were first domesticated. Canine domestication is thought to have occurred during the stone age.

Dogs and their symbolism are found in many cultures. They represent loyalty, protection, faithfulness, companionship, trust, protection, vigilance, guidance and courage. Druids believed dogs were the guardian of the mysteries and led people through the dark waters of the subconscious into light. They also offer blind love and obedience which symbolizes the sun, wind and fire and is believed to share the after-life with humans.

While most cultures regard the dog as a positive symbol, the Semitic and Muslim societies view the dog as evil, unclean or demonic. Dogs and women aren't allowed to enter Islamic shrines.

An ancient Semitic tradition is that the dog can see the angel of death approaching and he howls at the sight. Many Europeans believe that the dog howls because he can sense death and see the ghosts of departing people.

People who need this remedy are also full of strange impulses. They feel as though they might do something awful.

"Feels impelled to do reckless things, such as throwing the child, which he carries in his arms, through the window, and the like."

"Thought came into his mind to attack others in a mean way; to cut others with a knife he holds; to throw water he has in a tumbler into another's face."
— Hering

They are quite loquacious, *"delirium attended with constant talking. Makes speeches in his delirium; thinks he is a man of great authority. Incessant talking during night."* — Hering

If you take a tour of the repertory, you will see the following rubrics which are full of anger and violence but at the same time they repent very quickly after an outburst of violent rage:

MIND - ABRUPT - harsh
MIND - ABUSIVE
MIND - ANGER - violent
MIND - ATTACK others, desire to
MIND - BREAKING things
MIND - CRUELTY
MIND - HARDHEARTED
MIND - IMPULSE; morbid - reckless things; impelled to do
MIND - KILL; desire to
MIND - KILL; desire to - throw child; sudden impulse to - fire; into
MIND - RAGE
MIND - UNFEELING
MIND - WILDNESS

On further research, I have found that there are monsters and strange animals found in fairy tales throughout the world; the one thing they have in common is that they want to eat the human beings they find. For instance, the Bunyips of Australia who are described by natives as having a dog-like face, dark fur, a horse-like tail, flippers, and walrus-like tusks or horns. They are said to lurk in swamps, billabongs, creeks, riverbeds, and waterholes. It is amphibious and loves to catch women and children.

In the Japanese culture, there is believed to be the existence of Kappa ('river-child'). They are believed to be legendary creatures, a type of water spirit found in Japanese folklore. Some people say their faces are ape-like, while others show them with beaked visages, more like those of tortoises or with duck beaks.

Kappa supposedly inhabit the ponds and rivers of Japan. They catch swimming humans and eat them, from the inside out!

In Russia, an old story is told of the Baba Yaga, an ogress with stone teeth. Baba Yaga (Baba *Jaga*) is a witch-like character in Slavic folklore. She flies around on a giant mortar or broomstick, kidnaps and eats small children, and lives in a house which stands on chicken legs.

To sum up, I can say fairy tales are a combination of trolls, giants and dwarfs who can, either be benevolent or evil. In, stories like *'The Frog Prince'* and the *'Beauty and the Beast'* the main protagonist looks like he's the villain (ugly, hideous and repulsive), but in reality turns out to be the hero of the story.

Fairy tales not only teach us to consider the inter beauty of the person as in *'Beauty and the Beast,'* but also to understand the real meaning and emotions behind the beauty. Carl Jung in his book, *'Man and His Symbols,'* says, "Beauty redeems herself and her image of the masculine from the forces of repression, bringing to consciousness her capacity to trust her love, as something that combines spirit and nature in the best sense of the words."

I cannot finish this chapter of villains in fairy tales without mentioning *Belladonna*. It belongs, to the *Solanaceae*, or Nightshade family, and it's use can be traced back to ancient times.

According to Frans Vermeulen, *"The hallucinogenic Nightshade species from the Old World are called the hexing herbs because they were used in the ointments or flying potions of witches. Flying potions contained many substances, but typically Atropa belladonna, Datura stramonium, Hyoscyamus niger and Mandragora officinarum. The plants were mixed with fat – allegedly the fat of a dead child – to make an ointment, which was applied to various parts of the body, in particular the genital region and the anus. Because the genitals and anus have a rich supply of blood vessels, the hallucinogenic compounds were readily absorbed, inducing a deep, dream-filled sleep with dreams and visions of flying, dancing and having sexual orgies with the devil."*

"The use of belladonna can be traced back as far as written records go. In ancient Mesopotamia the Sumerians reportedly used it in the treatment of a number of illnesses thought to be caused by demons."

The intoxicating powers of the juice of the *Belladonna* plant were thought to be a contributing factor in inducing a state of frenzy in which the maenads tore apart animals, men and children. Legend also has it that, priests used to drink an infusion of the juice before they invoked the aid of Bellona, Goddess of War.

Dr H.C. Allen says, *"Belladonna* patients have plethoric constitutions; they are lively and entertaining when well, but violent and often delirious and wild when sick." All their emotions stir up suddenly like a storm, especially their anger, rage and violence. They may appear very frightening to an observer. If you see the symptoms below, you will get an impression of what I am talking about.

| MIND - ABRUPT - harsh |
| MIND - ABUSIVE |
| MIND - ANGER - violent |
| MIND - ATTACK others; desire to |

MIND - BREAKING things
MIND - CRUELTY
MIND - HARDHEARTED
MIND - IMPULSE; morbid - reckless things; impelled to do
MIND - KILL; desire to
MIND - KILL; desire to - throw child; sudden impulse to - fire; into
MIND - RAGE
MIND - UNFEELING
MIND - WILDNESS
MIND - ANGER - sudden
MIND - BARKING - delirium, during
MIND - BITING - delirium, during
MIND - BREAKING things - desire to break things
MIND - CRUELTY - loves to make people and animals suffer
MIND - CUNNING
MIND - DECEITFUL
MIND - DELIRIUM - bite, desire to
MIND - DELIRIUM - face - red
MIND - DELIRIUM - fierce
MIND - DELIRIUM - loquacious
MIND - DELIRIUM - terror, expressive of
MIND - DELIRIUM - wild
MIND - DELUSIONS - body - cut through; he is
MIND - DELUSIONS - devil - sees
MIND - DELUSIONS - dogs - sees
MIND - DELUSIONS - figures - seeing figures
MIND - DELUSIONS - people - behind him; someone is
MIND - DESTRUCTIVENESS
MIND - ESCAPE, attempts to - delirium; during
MIND - IMPULSE; morbid - run; to

MIND - INSANITY - anger, from
MIND - INSANITY - break pins; she will sit and
MIND - INSANITY - malicious
MIND - INSANITY - strength; with increased
MIND - JEALOUSY
MIND - KICKING - anger; during
MIND - KILL; desire to - car; by running into people with her
MIND - MANIA - demonic
MIND - MANIA - rage, with
MIND - MANIA - violence, with deeds of
MIND - RAGE - biting, with
MIND - RAGE - chained, had to be
MIND - RAGE - malicious
MIND - RAGE - touch, renewed by
MIND - RAGE - violent

Late Dr Ananda Zaren said in one of her articles, "*Where Stramonium patients may act as if pursued by a frightening beast, Belladonna individuals become enraged like a beast and can have behaviours that are animal-like.*"

Their episodes of rage can include symptoms of grunting, grimacing, increased strength and barking and growling like a dog."

I spoke above of the anima (the feminine aspect of man) mainly highlighting the negative side. The negative animus, often appears in myths, folk tales and fairy tales as a death demon, or death personified. In other fairy tales the animus plays the role of a robber or a murderer.

One example of this is '*Bluebeard*' (French – '*La Barbe bleue*'). It is a French literary fairy tale written by Charles Perrault. The tale tells the story of a violent nobleman in the habit of murdering his wives and the attempts of one wife to avoid the fate of her predecessors. *Gilles de Rais, a fifteenth century aristocrat* and prolific serial killer, has been suggested as the source for the character of Bluebeard as has Conomor the Accused, an early Breton king. 'The White Dove,' 'Mister Fox' and 'Fitcher's Bird' are tales similar to 'Bluebeard' who secretly kills all his wives in a hidden chamber.

Jung says, "In this form, the animus incarnates all those semi-conscious, depressing, gloomy, indifferent and destructive reflections that invade a woman when she has failed to realize some obligation of feeling."

Whenever one of these personifications of the unconscious takes possession of our mind, the ego starts to identify with them to the point where it is unable to detach them and see them for what they are.

In homoeopathy, the 'mental state' in which the patient finds himself can be matched to it's simillimum to restore consonance. As Hahnemann said very clearly in his magnum opus 'Organon of Medicine' (sixth edition) under aphorism 210-211, "Mental diseases do not constitute a class of disease sharply separated from all others, since in all other so-called corporeal diseases the condition of the disposition and mind is always altered; in all cases of disease we are called on to cure, the state of the patient's disposition is to be particularly noted, along with the totality of the symptoms, if we would trace an accurate picture of the disease, in order to be able therefrom to treat it homoeopathically with success."

"This holds good to such an extent, that the state of the disposition of the patient often chiefly determines the selection of the homoeopathic remedy, as being a decidedly characteristic symptom which can least of all remain concealed from the accurately observing physician."

Kent always said, "there are no diseases, but only sick people." The mental symptoms of a remedy are very crucial because it represents will, understanding and his unconscious mind that makes a person what he or she is.

In relation to children and fairy tales, Bettelheim has said: "Parents who wish to deny that their child has murderous wishes and wants to tear things and even *people into pieces, believe that their child must be prevented from engaging in such thoughts. On the other hand, learning that others have the same or similar fantasies makes us feel that we are a part of humanity, and that allays our fear for having such destructive ideas."*

Parents wish to believe that if their child sees them as a witch or a giant, it has nothing to do with them, but is the result of the strong influence fairy tales have on them. Research has shown, however, that the mind of a young child is filled with anxiety, rage and insecurities. Unconsciously due to the behaviour and attitude of their parents, some children may unconsciously mention that their father is a giant or their mother is a witch.

CHAPTER 22

Further Reading and Research....

Reading and researching myths and fairy tales provides a wealth of information about the pathways in and out of abusive situations. Creative thinkers can play with the symbolism in these stories and find new ways to approach their own story. If you want to play with fairy tales then you can search for a recent translation of Grimm's Tales for Young and Old, translated by Ralph Manheim; it is a good place to start off from. Older versions were often Christianized and sanitized, and lack the juice of more accurate translations.

- For issues with the father I would recommend the readers to read: *Rapunzel, The Girl without Hands, Rumpelstiltskin, Thousand Furs, Old Rink Rank, Maid Maleen*

- For issues with the mother: *The Three Little Men in the Woods, Mother Holle, Darling Roland, Ashputtle (Cinderella), One-eye, Two-eyes and Three-eyes, Little Brother and Little Sister, Hansel and Gretel, The Lamb and the Fish*

If you wish to explore different ways to interpret the symbolism in stories and fairy tales, I would recommend seeking out the following books: *The Wounded Woman: Healing the Father-Daughter Relationship* (Shambhala, 1983), *On the Way to the Wedding: Transforming the Love Relationship* (Shambhala, 1986), and *Meeting the Madwoman: An Inner Challenge for Feminine Spirit* (Shambhala, 1993), all by Linda Schierse Leonard, PhD; and *Women Who Run with the Wolves: Myths and Stories of the Wild Woman Archetype*, by Clarissa Pinkola Estes, PhD (Ballantine Books, 1992). Although each of these books explores different areas of life that may be of interest to survivors, all of them utilize the symbolism in modern and ancient stories to explore the life-affirming pathways and options that have been available to humanity since the beginning of time. All of these books can help you learn how to work with the symbolism in fairy tales (and in your own life), and are wonderful healing tools in and of themselves.

Some interesting books written by Marie-Louise Von Franz which I find interesting are:

- Alchemical Active Imagination Alchemy: An Introduction to the Symbolism and the Psychology

- Animus and Anima in Fairy Tales

- The Cat: A Tale of Feminine Redemption

- Archetypal Dimensions of the Psyche

- Archetypal Patterns in Fairy Tales

- Creation Myths , Patterns of Creativity Mirrored in Creation Myths

- Dreams: A Study of the Dreams of Jung, Descartes, Socrates and Other Historical Figures

- The Feminine in Fairy Tales

- The Golden Ass of Apuleius: The Liberation of the Feminine in Man

- Individuation in Fairytales C. G. Jung: His Myth in Our Time

- An Introduction to the Interpretation of Fairy Tales

- Jung's Typology Lectures on Jung's Typology with essay on 'The Inferior Function'

- Light from the Darkness- The Art of Peter Birkhauser

- Number and Time: Reflections Leading Towards a Unification of Depth Psychology and Physics

- On Divination and Synchronicity: The Psychology of Meaningful Chance

- On Dreams and Death: A Jungian Interpretation

- The Passion of Perpetua: A Psychological Interpretation of Her Vision

- Projection and Re-collection in Jungian Psychology: Reflections of the Soul

- Puer Aeternus: A Psychological Study of the Adult Struggle with the Paradise of Childhood

- The Psychological Meaning of Redemption Motifs in Fairy Tales

- Shadow and Evil in Fairy Tales

- Time, Rhythm and Repose (Art and Imagination)

- The Way of the Dream

  Some other works who I found useful in my learning process are:

- Encounters With the Soul: Active Imagination as Developed by C. G. Jung, by Barbara Hannah

- The Grail Legend by Emma Jung

- In the Wake of Jung: A Selection from Harvest edited by Molly Tuby

- Lilith-The First Eve: Historical and Psychological Aspects of the Dark Feminine by Siegmund Hurwitz

- Man and His Symbols by C.J. Jung

- Meetings with Jung: Conversations Recorded During the Years, 1946-1961 by E.A. Bennet

- The Mother: Archetypal Image in Fairy Tales by Sibylle Birkhauser-oeri.

Homoeopathic Books

- Chronic Diseases, S. Hahnemann. B.Jain Publishers, New Delhi, India

- Synoptic Reference, Frans Vermeulen, B. Jain Archibel, New Delhi, India

- Concordant Reference Complete Classic Materia Medica, B.Jain Archibel, New Delhi, India

- Organon of Medicine 6th Edn., S. Hahnemann., B.Jain Publishers, New Delhi, India

- Homeopathic Psychology, Philip M Bailey, B.Jain Publishers, New Delhi, India

- Encyclopedia of Materia Medica, Dr H.C. Allen

- Essay on Homeopathy Psyche and Substance, Edward C Whitmount, B.Jain Publishers, New Delhi, India

- Repertory of Homeopathic Materia Medica, James Tyler Kent, B.Jain Publishers, New Delhi, India

- A Dictionary of Practical Materia Medica - 3 Vols, J.H. Clarke, B.Jain Publishers, New Delhi, India

- A Study of Materia Medica, N.M. Choudhari, B.Jain Publishers, New Delhi, India

- Portraits of Homoeopathic Medicines, Catherine Coulter

  I buy all my books from the following addresses:

- www.amazon.com

- www.bjain.com

- www.alibris.com

- www.barnesandnoble.com